Secondary Market Price Guide
& Collector Handbook
FIRST EDITION

Let's Get Together – #CD006
This adorable figurine is available exclusively as a
Symbol Of Membership gift to Dreamsicles Club members in 1998!

This publication is *not* affiliated with the Dreamsicles Club™, Cast Art Industries, Inc. or any of their affiliates, subsidiaries, distributors or representatives. Any opinions expressed are solely those of the authors, and do not necessarily reflect those of Cast Art Industries, Inc. The market values listed in this guide are based on compilations of current market trends, but the publisher assumes no liability or responsibility for any loss incurred by users of this guide due to variable market conditions. "Dreamsicles®" is a registered trademark of Cast Art Industries, Inc. All Dreamsicles® artwork is the copyrighted property of Cast Art Industries, Inc., Corona, California.

Front cover: "The Flying Lesson"

Back cover (top to bottom): "Cherub And Child" *and* "Dream Team"

Managing Editor:	Jeff Mahony	Art Director:	Joe T. Nguyen
	jeff@collectorspub.com		*joe@collectorspub.com*
Associate Editor:	Jan Cronan	Staff Artists:	Scott Sierakowski
Editorial Assistants:	Gia C. Manalio		David Ten Eyck
	Melissa Bennett		Lance Doyle
	Scarlet H. Riley	Contributing Artist:	Joni Walker
	Nicole W. Blasenak		
Contributing Editor:	Mike Micciulla		

ISBN 1-888914-12-2

Collectors' Publishing Co., Inc.
598 Pomeroy Avenue
Meriden, CT 06450
http://www.collectorspub.com

CONTENTS

COLLECTOR'S
VALUE GUIDE™

CONTENTS

Foreword by Kristin Haynes

Dear Friend,

Welcome to the very first edition of the Collector's Value Guide for Dreamsicles. I am pleased and honored that a prestigious company like Collectors' Publishing has seen fit to produce this wonderful handbook about Dreamsicles.

For several years now, Dreamsicles fans and collectors have been asking if we could produce a color catalog for the collector showing individual pieces. This new 1998 Value Guide goes several steps beyond that. It provides full color pictures of every Dreamsicles figurine that Cast Art has ever produced. Plus, the book features lots of accessory items, Dreamsicles history and gift-giving ideas in a well organized format.

I am delighted that the Dreamsicles Club has decided to provide each member with one of these beautiful and informative books as a benefit of membership. We look forward to updating this guide every year as new designs are introduced. Who knows? The book itself may even become collectible in its own right!

My thanks to all of you for your letters of support and encouragement. I feel honored that my sculptures have earned a valued place in your homes and in your lives, and I look forward to many more years of sharing Dreamsicles with all of you.

Happy Collecting!

Kristin

COLLECTOR'S
VALUE GUIDE™

Introducing The Collector's Value Guide™

Welcome to a new collecting tradition, the first edition of the Dreamsicles® Value Guide! Whether you're a first-time collector or have been a fan of artist Kristin Haynes' fabulous cherubs, children and animals since their 1991 debut, the Collector's Value Guide has plenty to offer. With full-color photographs of every Dreamsicles piece ever produced, the Value Guide is the most comprehensive source of Dreamsicles information around. Inside you'll find answers to all of your Dreamsicles questions, as well as fun sections designed to enhance your collecting pleasure:

- A preview of the 1998 Dreamsicles in our "What's New" section.
- Spotlights on the "Original 29" Dreamsicles and Limited Editions.
- A look at the history of the Dreamsicles Club.
- A great gift ideas section; plus fun display tips.
- An "at-a-glance" checklist of recent retirements.
- Biography of Dreamsicles artist Kristin Haynes.
- An informative section on insuring your collection.

The Collector's Value Guide is the best way to keep track of all aspects of your collection. With important information such as issue year, status and style number presented in an easy-to-follow format, the Value Guide provides all the tools you'll need to keep an accurate record of your ever-growing Dreamsicles collection. In addition to this information, the guide will walk readers through the workings of the secondary market – an exciting feature for those interested in the value of their collection. Up-to-date secondary market values have been gathered from a wide range of sources from all over the country and are a benchmark that collectors can use to price their pieces for resale, for insurance purposes or just for fun. Best of all, the Value Guide is designed as a worksheet so you can record the market values of your pieces to discover just how much your collection is worth.

The easy-to-use Collector's Value Guide is a dream come true, making your Dreamsicles collection more fun than ever!

COLLECTOR'S
VALUE GUIDE™

The popular Dreamsicles line from Cast Art Industries has been warming the hearts of collectors ever since it was first introduced in 1991. Designed by artist Kristin Haynes, the adorable cherubs and animals began showing up in homes across the country as holiday and birthday presents, and by the following year were one of the best-selling gift items in the nation. The Dreamsicles collection has grown from 29 pieces to about 1,000 in less than a decade, with most of the collection featuring the inspirational cherubs that people everywhere have fallen in love with.

With beautiful eyes, chubby cheeks, pudgy noses and shy smiles, the endearing winged children make you just want to take them home! The cherubs engage in a wide variety of earthly and celestial activities, such as playing games, frolicking with friends or riding rainbows. Other pieces portray cherubs as they reach the milestones of life, like the first day of school, graduation, or marriage.

Berry Cute
Dreamsicles Cherubs

Most of the cherubs wear pastel wreaths around their heads made from dried wildflowers and ribbons, creating a natural handcrafted look. Cast Art has also released a wide array of holiday-themed cherubs. While the "year-round" figurines feature traditional pastel wreaths, the "holiday" figurines feature wreaths dotted with poinsettias and berries. Many early Dreamsicles figurines were issued in both styles with separate style numbers.

While it is the cherubs that most people are familiar with, the Dreamsicles collection also features a diverse assortment of animals. The whimsical Dreamsicles animals have made up a large part of the collection from the beginning. In fact, there are now 40 bunnies in the collection, as well as 12 mice, 10 cows, 10 pigs, 9 bears and many more to choose from. Beyond animals, there are also Santas, elves, witches, goblins and mermaids – almost anything the mind can dream up!

Bunny Bouquet
Dreamsicles Animals

COLLECTOR'S
VALUE GUIDE™

Dreamsicles Overview

The Dreamsicles line also features *Heavenly Classics*, a wonderful marriage of Kristin Haynes' cherubs and Cast Art artists Steve and Gigi Hackett's traditional angels. There are now over 25 of these beautiful designs, which were first introduced in 1995. In 1996, the playful *Dreamsicles Kids* were introduced with colorful clothes and irresistible faces.

Higher Learning
Heavenly Classics

Pop Goes The Weasel
Dreamsicles Kids

Dreamsicles enthusiasts got a sneak peek at some of these child characters when they appeared along with cherubs in the 1995 "Dreamsicles and Me" series. Over 50 *Dreamsicles Kids* figurines were introduced in the first two years of this exciting new feature of the collection.

As more Dreamsicles figurines are retired or suspended, some of the older pieces are beginning to increase in value on the secondary market. Among the more coveted pieces are the elaborate limited editions that have been released each year since 1992 and are limited to a specific quantity. Annual Christmas limited editions have also been released since 1992 and are limited to one year of production. Exclusive figurines are also available to members of the rapidly-growing Dreamsicles Club, formed by Cast Art in 1993.

More and more people are discovering the magic of Dreamsicles each year and the appeal isn't limited to just figurines! The elaborate Dreamsicles musicals and waterglobes have become a very popular part of the collection and the cherub theme has been incorporated into bells, ornaments, plates and much more.

Whether for gift-giving or collecting, Dreamsicles are a great way to celebrate life's special occasions. Kristin Haynes' inspirational cherubs have struck a chord with people everywhere with their childlike innocence and imaginative designs. As the collection continues to grow, it's an exciting time for Dreamsicles fans, now and for years to come!

COLLECTOR'S
VALUE GUIDE™

What's New For Dreamsicles

This section highlights the new 1998 releases for the Dreamsicles collection. There are 70 exciting releases for Spring 1998, including 58 cherub figurines, five musicals, two bookends and five eggs.

LIMITED EDITIONS AND EVENT FIGURINES

Handmade With Love . . . This limited edition features three cherubs hard at work on a thick, fluffy quilt fashioned of pastel colors and gold stars. The quilt must be made from the cloud upon which it rests, since these heavenly workers surely have plucked the stars from the sky for this masterpiece!

Handmade With Love
Limited Edition

All Aboard! . . . Two adorable cherubs have donned wreaths made of holly leaves and poinsettia blossoms and hopped on board the "Holiday Express" to help Santa complete his rounds. The train glides over a blanket of glistening snow, and is painted in festive holiday colors. This Christmas-lover's delight even comes equipped with cookies and candy canes for wheels. This piece is the seventh Dreamsicles *Christmas Limited Edition* figurine, and will surely make a welcome addition to your holiday decorations each and every year!

All Aboard!
Christmas Limited Edition

A Day Of Fun . . . This happy-go-lucky little guy is off to have some fun on a beautiful summer day! The pink and blue balloons he holds seem to fly out behind him as he and his puppy pal frolic on the bright green grass. This figurine is available only during Dreamsicles Day events. Check your local retailer for details so you can enjoy this annual "day of fun" with other Dreamsicles fans.

A Day Of Fun
Dreamsicles Day Figurine

COLLECTOR'S
VALUE GUIDE™

What's New For Dreamsicles

CHERUBS

1001 Baby Names . . . Two celestial cuties whisper suggestions to a young mother-to-be as she reads through the book "1001 Baby Names."

Baked With Love . . . Wearing a baker's hat instead of the usual dried floral wreath, this Dreamsicles sweetie has baked cookies for a loved one, who looks ready to gobble them up.

The Baptism . . . A friendly-looking cherub assists a young child during a baptism ceremony, while a feathered friend sits nearby.

Birthday Fun . . . It's not clear who's having the birthday here – the little cherub or the puppy! Either way, they both seem content in sharing a yummy-looking birthday cake.

Blocks of Love . . . This charming little seraph is too shy to say it, so he's spelled out his feelings with blocks: "I ❤ U."

Daydreamin' . . . This cherub looks like he has a lot on his mind as he sits musing. From his expression, it looks like they're all happy thoughts!

Dream On . . . In this treasure, a charming little angel has fallen asleep in a soft, fluffy cloud. Was it a hard day of work or play that tired him out?

Easter Artist . . . A fuzzy-haired bunny looks on as a cherub works hard at getting just the right designs on his collection of Easter eggs.

1001 Baby Names	Baked With Love	The Baptism	Birthday Fun
Blocks Of Love	Daydreamin'	Dream On	Easter Artist

COLLECTOR'S
VALUE GUIDE™

Easter Basket . . . A festive little angel sits right in an Easter basket and waits to become an Easter surprise for some lucky Dreamsicles collector.

Get Well Wishes . . . This poor little angel is home sick in bed when she should be out having fun! She'll be back on her feet again very soon though: she's feeling better already just reading her "Get Well" card.

Heart On A String and *Here's My Heart . . .* Both of these cuties hold tight to the strings of heart-shaped balloons and look hopeful that their sweethearts get the message.

Home Sweet Home . . . A white-haired kitten plays with a ball of yarn as her cherub companion works on a quilt bearing the message "Home Sweet Home."

Ice Dancing . . . This figurine consists of an adorable little cherub dressed up in her best ice skating outfit. A penguin friend, who's surely at home on the ice, accompanies her.

Little Leaguer . . . A great gift for any aspiring baseball "star," this little cherub has caught a star-shaped baseball in his trusty mitt!

Love My Bunny and *Love My Lamb . . .* Each of these two figurines features a charming little angel cuddling with his favorite stuffed pal.

Love You Sew . . . This treasure depicts a smiling cherub hard at work on a needlepoint pattern, as a fuzzy-haired kitten sits by.

Easter Basket   Get Well Wishes   Heart On A String   Here's My Heart   Home Sweet Home

Ice Dancing   Little Leaguer   Love My Bunny   Love My Lamb   Love You Sew

What's New For Dreamsicles

Matchmaker . . . A smiling cherub fills in for Cupid as he gives courage to a little boy presenting a flower to his girl.

Mom's Garden . . . A Dreamsicles cherub leans over a fence to water a flower garden while a feathered friend looks on. This would make a lovely gift for any mother, as the flower garden forms the word "Mom."

Moonstruck . . . A friendly cherub sits on a cloud and hugs the smiling crescent moon as it passes through the night skies.

Mother's Helper . . . A heavenly visitor stands watch over a baby in his cradle, whose blocks spell out exactly for whom he's waiting: "Mom."

Music Makers . . . An old-fashioned Victrola fills the heavens with beautiful music as a cherub and his friend roll out the musical selections.

Peaceful Dreams . . . This little angel must have really been tired! Luckily, she's found a place to rest on this fluffy cloud, with a pink blanket to keep her warm.

Playground Pony . . . This li'l pardner has put on his cowboy boots and ten-gallon hat and set out on a long trail ride. He'll have to use his imagination, though, as his steed is merely a rocking horse!

Please Be Mine . . . A cherub smiles as he patiently awaits his sweetheart's response to the request on his heart-shaped balloon: "Be Mine."

| Matchmaker | Mom's Garden | Moonstruck | Mother's Helper |

| Music Makers | Peaceful Dreams | Playground Pony | Please Be Mine |

COLLECTOR'S
VALUE GUIDE™

What's New For Dreamsicles

Pray For Peace . . . This hopeful little angel sits perched atop a globe, praying for peace on earth.

Pretty Posies . . . This charming little angel looks like he's just done some gardening, or he's at least been picking the flowers: he has an armful of them just for you!

Songbirds . . . This joyful figurine would be perfect for any music lover. It features a cherub seated atop a wall of musical notes, belting out a tune along with two fuzzy-topped songbirds.

Stardust . . . A Dreamsicles cherub hugs a shimmering star that he's plucked from the sky.

A Stroll In The Park . . . A pair of protective cherubs surround a baby carriage and the newborn inside, as the new mother heads out for "A Stroll In The Park."

Sun Shower . . . The warm sun peeks out as a Dreamsicles cherub takes a ride on a cloud.

We Are Winning . . . This cherub stands upon a light blue cloud and holds a silver trophy containing yellow daffodils. Proceeds from the sale of this figurine are donated to the American Cancer Society, whose symbol can be seen at the cherub's feet.

| Pray For Peace | Pretty Posies | Songbirds | Stardust |
| A Stroll In The Park | Sun Shower | We Are Winning | |

COLLECTOR'S
VALUE GUIDE™

What's New For Dreamsicles

Dreamsicles Expressions . . . This new group of Dreamsicles features those lovable baby angels, each with a fuzzy-haired puppy and a big red heart. The white lettering on the symbol of love profess heartfelt attraction to someone special.

Forever Friends

Grandma I Love You

I Love You

Mother I Love You   Sister I Love You

You're Special

Dreamsicles Nursery Rhymes . . . The Dreamsicles cherubs have entered storyland! This new series features four figurines, each depicting a well-known scene from a children's nursery rhyme. There are cherubs jumping over the moon with the cow from "Hey Diddle Diddle," sitting on the wall with "Humpty Dumpty," assisting Jack as he jumps over the candlestick and helping to console "Little Bo Peep" who's lost her sheep.

Hey Diddle Diddle

Humpty Dumpty

Jumping Jack

Little Bo Peep

Dreamsicles Pals . . . The cherubs are coming . . . and they're bringing their friends! This new group of Dreamsicles features 12 miniature cherubs, each with their own animal pal.

Bunny Pal   Cow Pal   Doggie Pal   Duckie Pal   Elephant Pal   Kitty Pal

Lambie Pal   Monkey Pal   Panda Pal   Penguin Pal   Piggy Pal   Unicorn Pal

COLLECTOR'S
VALUE GUIDE™

OTHER DREAMSICLES COLLECTIBLES

Dreamsicles Musicals . . . In "Birthday Surprise," the song "My Favorite Things" accompanies a little angel as he surprises his friend on her birthday. Cherubs and animals have a delightful time among clouds and rainbows in "Cherub Twirler," and "Flying High" displays a soaring baby angel, who has recently graduated from flight school. "Sleep Tight" plays "Rock-A-Bye Baby" and features a toddler asleep in her bassinet, guarded by a Dreamsicles cherub and his bunny pal. "Together Forever" features a young bride and groom on their wedding day, with two well-wishing cherubs seated nearby.

| Birthday Surprise | Cherub Twirler | Flying High | Sleep Tight | Together Forever |

Dreamsicles Bookends . . . For the literary type who needs some celestial assistance with their reading material, there are two new sets of cherub bookends available. Each features two scholarly cherubs poised, quill pen in hand, musing over what to write after the words "Once upon a time..."

Cherub Bookends (blue)   Cherub Bookends (pink)

Dreamsicles Eggs . . . Each of these five new egg-shaped figurines features a heart-warming scene inside. From the "Sweethearts Egg," which contains two courting cherubs, to the "Snuggle Blanket Egg," with its warm and cozy angel inside, you're bound to be reminded of nothing but pure innocence, whichever egg you choose!

| Heaven's Little Helper Egg | Join The Fun Egg | Merry-Go-Round Egg | Snuggle Blanket Egg | Sweethearts Egg |

Recent Retirements & Suspensions

Each year, Cast Art announces the "retirement" or "suspension" of several Dreamsicles designs. Those pieces that are retired will never be produced again, while the suspended pieces may be brought back into production. Both retired and suspended pieces are still available through retailers until each store's stock is sold out. The list below chronicles the 1997 cherub figurine retirements and suspensions in the Dreamsicles collection. Of note, although not listed here, all of the *Heavenly Classics* figurines were either retired or suspended in 1997, except for "New Beginnings" and "Sounds Of Heaven." If you need to add any of these figurines to your collection, you'd better act fast!

1997 CHERUB RETIREMENTS

Club, Limited Edition & Event Figurines
- ❑ Free Spirit (1997, #CD005, *Club Symbol Of Membership Figurine*)
- ❑ Happy Landings (1997, #10156, *Limited Edition of 5,000*)
- ❑ Heavenly Flowers (1996, #CD104, *Club Members-Only Figurine*)
- ❑ Homeward Bound (1996, #DX251, *Christmas Limited Edition*)
- ❑ The Golden Rule (1997, #E9701, *Dreamsicles Day Figurine*)
- ❑ Sleigh Bells Ring (1997, #10187, *Limited Edition of 2,500*)
- ❑ Time To Retire (1996, #DD103, *Dreamsicles Day Figurine*)

Cherubs
- ❑ Catch A Falling Star (1993, #DC166)
- ❑ Daffodil Days (1996, #DC343, *American Cancer Society Figurine*)

Daffodil Days (#DC343)

Cherubs, cont.
- ❑ Gecko Guava (1996, #10005)
- ❑ Get Well Soon (1995, #DC244)
- ❑ Hugabye Baby (1995, #DC701)
- ❑ Love My Kitty (1993, #DC130)
- ❑ Love My Puppy (1993, #DC131)
- ❑ Love My Teddy (1993, #DC132)
- ❑ Moon Dance (1994, #DC210)
- ❑ P. S. I Love You (1993, #DC203)
- ❑ Poetry In Motion (1995, #DC113)
- ❑ Searching For Hope (1997, #DC019)
- ❑ Teacher's Pet (1993, #DC124)
- ❑ Thinking Of You (1993, #DC129)
- ❑ Twinkle, Twinkle (1995, #DC700)

Holiday Cherubs
- ❑ Hugabye Baby (1995, #DX701)
- ❑ Moon Dance (1995, #DX210)
- ❑ Poetry In Motion (1995, #DX113)
- ❑ Teacher's Pet (1993, #DX124)
- ❑ Thinking Of You (1993, #DX129)
- ❑ Twinkle, Twinkle (1995, #DX700)

1997 CHERUB SUSPENSIONS

Cherubs
- ❑ Star Power (Early Release – Fall 1997, #10128)
- ❑ Together Again (Early Release – Fall 1997, #10246)

COLLECTOR'S
VALUE GUIDE™

Recent Retirements & Suspensions

Here's more exciting news for Dreamsicles collectors! The following is a list of Dreamsicles cherubs that were designated for retirement or suspension by Cast Art Industries at the end of 1997. The official status of each figurine had not been determined at the time of this printing. These pieces are listed as "Ret./Susp.: 1997" in the Value Guide section. Check with your local Dreamsicles retailer for details!

OTHER 1997 CHERUB RETIREMENTS/SUSPENSIONS

Cherubs
- ❑ All Better Now (1995, #DC246)
- ❑ Baby And Me (1994, #DC054)
- ❑ Baby Steps (1996, #DC415)
- ❑ Bar Mitzvah Boy (1995, #DC408)
- ❑ Birdie And Me (1994, #DC056)
- ❑ Born This Day (1994, #DC230)
- ❑ Brown Baggin' (1996, #DC716)
- ❑ Bunny And Me (1994, #DC055)
- ❑ Burning Love (1995, #DC220)
- ❑ The Christening (1995, #DC300)
- ❑ Cupid's Arrow (1994, #DC199)
- ❑ Don't Rock The Boat (1995, #DC404)
- ❑ Dreidel, Dreidel (1995, #DC302)
- ❑ Easy Rider (1996, #DC414)
- ❑ Feet First (1996, #DC320)
- ❑ First Communion (1995, #DC301)
- ❑ Forty Winks (1995, #DC233)
- ❑ Free Bird (1995, #DC234)
- ❑ Get Better Soon (1995, #DC245)
- ❑ God Bless America (1995, #DC706)

Cherubs, cont.
- ❑ Grand Old Flag (1995, #DC232)
- ❑ Haley (1996, #DC321)
- ❑ Hang Loose (1996, #10004)
- ❑ Have A Heart (1994, #DC198)
- ❑ Hawaiian Love Song (1996, #10003)

A Kiss In Time (#DC309)

- ❑ Hello Dolly (1995, #DC702)
- ❑ Joyful Gathering (1994, #DC231)
- ❑ Joyful Noise (1996, #DC409)
- ❑ A Kiss In Time (1995, #DC309)
- ❑ Kitty And Me (1994, #DC051)
- ❑ Let's Play Fetch (1995, #DC237)
- ❑ Lullaby (1994, #DC173)
- ❑ Mermaid's Gift (1996, #10002)
- ❑ Moonglow (1995, #DC235)
- ❑ 'Nite 'Nite (1995, #DC238)
- ❑ Northern Exposure (1996, #DC420)
- ❑ Over The Rainbow (1994, #DC209)
- ❑ Piano Lesson (1995, #DC413)
- ❑ Puppy And Me (1994, #DC052)
- ❑ Purr-fect Pals (1995, #DC239)

Don't Rock The Boat (#DC404)

COLLECTOR'S
VALUE GUIDE™

Recent Retirements & Suspensions

Cherubs, cont.
- ☐ Rainbow Rider (1995, #DC236)
- ☐ Share The Fun (1994, #DC178)
- ☐ Shipmates (1996, #10001)
- ☐ Skater's Waltz (1995, #DC412)
- ☐ Star Gazers (1995, #DC308)

Shipmates (#10001)

- ☐ A Star In One (1996, #DC318)
- ☐ Starlight, Starbright (1995, #DC708)
- ☐ Straight From The Heart (1996, #DC314)
- ☐ Sugarfoot (1994, #DC167)
- ☐ Super Star (1995, #DC704)
- ☐ Sweet Charity (1995, #DC411)
- ☐ Sweethearts (1994, #DC200)
- ☐ Swing On A Star (1994, #DC208)
- ☐ Teddy And Me (1994, #DC053)
- ☐ Tender Loving Care (1995, #DC247)
- ☐ Three Amigos (1994, #DC179)
- ☐ Tiny Dancer (1993, #DC165)
- ☐ Twosome (1996, #DC149)
- ☐ We're Best Friends (1996, #DC715)
- ☐ Winger (1996, #DC319)
- ☐ Wistful Thinking (1995, #DC707)
- ☐ You've Got A Friend (1994, #DC170)

Holiday Cherubs
- ☐ Baby And Me (1994, #DX054)
- ☐ Baby's First Christmas (1994, #DX242)
- ☐ Bedtime Prayer (1995, #DX703)
- ☐ Birdie And Me (1994, #DX056)

Holiday Cherubs, cont.
- ☐ Bunny And Me (1994, #DX055)
- ☐ Christmas Morning (1995, #DX710)
- ☐ Christmas Trim (1996, #DX711)
- ☐ Come Let Us Adore Him (1995, #DX475)
- ☐ Good Shepherd (1994, #DX104)
- ☐ Hello Dolly (1995, #DX702)
- ☐ Here Comes Trouble (1992, #DX214)
- ☐ Holiday Pals (1995, #DX709)
- ☐ Kitty And Me (1994, #DX051)
- ☐ Noel (1996, #DX712)
- ☐ Oh Little Star (1996, #DX713)
- ☐ Open Me First (1994, #DX243)
- ☐ Puppy And Me (1994, #DX052)
- ☐ Santa's Little Helper (1991, #DX109)
- ☐ Sleigh Ride (1992, #DX122)
- ☐ Starlight, Starbright (1995, #DX708)
- ☐ Super Star (1995, #DX704)
- ☐ Teddy And Me (1994, #DX053)
- ☐ Wistful Thinking (1995, #DX707)

Oh Little Star (#DX713)

Look in the Value Guide section for other 1997 Dreamsicles retirements and suspensions, including *Heavenly Classics*, *Dreamsicles Kids*, *Animals* and more!

COLLECTOR'S
VALUE GUIDE™

THE BIRTH OF DREAMSICLES

In March 1991, the "Original 29" Dreamsicles created by Kristin Haynes were shipped to retail stores around the country. These trailblazing figurines, which included six cherubs, four musicians and 19 animals, were simpler in design than most of today's Dreamsicles releases. Many Dreamsicles collectors hold a special place in their hearts (and in their homes) for these "firsts," though, sadly, all 29 figurines have now been retired or suspended.

Interestingly, the "Original 29" were introduced without names! Instead, the pieces were referred to in short descriptive phrases, such as "Medium Sitting Cherub With Lamb" or "Standing Cow." Each figurine was eventually assigned a name by Cast Art, with the exception of the four musician figurines and "Small Cherub With Hanging Ribbon," which were all suspended in 1992.

THE FIRST SIX CHERUBS

The appeal of Dreamsicles cherubs was quickly evident, as the first six cherubs were introduced with engaging smiles and handcrafted wreaths.

Best Pals
Retired 1994

Forever Friends
Retired 1994

Forever Yours
Retired 1995

Mischief Maker
Retired 1996

Sitting Pretty
Retired 1996

Small Cherub With Hanging Ribbon
Suspended 1992

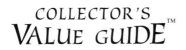

COLLECTOR'S
VALUE GUIDE™

Spotlight On The "Original 29"

THE MUSICIANS

The four musician figurines released among the "Original 29" are a departure from the rest of the Dreamsicles collection. These colorful figurines may be the early "forerunners" of the Dreamsicles Kids, who made their debut in 1996.

Musician With Cymbals	Musician With Drums	Musician With Flute	Musician With Trumpet
Suspended 1992	*Suspended 1992*	*Suspended 1992*	*Suspended 1992*

THE BUNNIES

There were seven bunnies among the "Original 29" figurines. Even today, rabbits are the most prolific of Haynes' Dreamicles animal designs and number more than 40 in the Dreamsicles collection.

Bunny Hop	Hippity Hop	Honey Bun	Mr. Bunny
Retired 1995	*Retired 1994*	*Retired 1995*	*Retired 1994*

Mrs. Bunny	Santa Bunny	Tiny Bunny
Retired 1994	*Retired 1994*	*Retired 1995*

COLLECTOR'S
VALUE GUIDE™

Spotlight On The "Original 29"

THE OTHER ANIMALS

The *"Original 29" also featured a dozen other Dreamsicles animals, including an armadillo, two bears, two cows, three lambs, two mice and two pigs. Many fun animal designs have since followed.*

Armadillo
Suspended 1992

Buddy Bear
Retired 1994

Mama Bear
Retired 1994

Dairy Delight
Retired 1995

Sweet Cream
Retired 1996

Lambie Pie
Retired 1994

Mutton Chops
Retired 1994

Wooley Bully
Retired 1994

Mother Mouse
Retired 1994

P. J. Mouse
Retired 1994

Pigmalion
Retired 1995

Pigtails
Retired 1995

Limited Editions

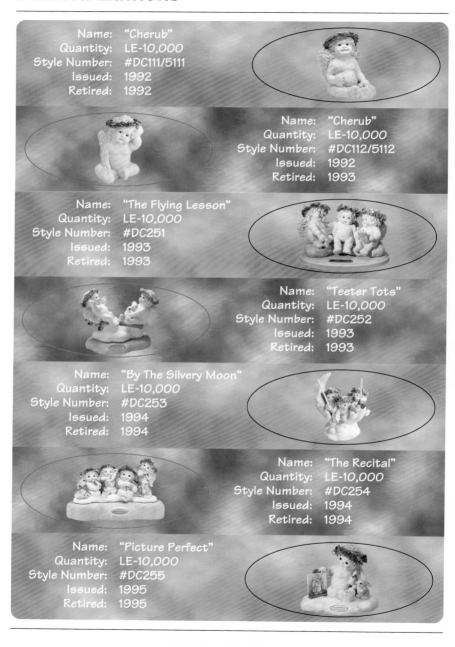

Name: "Cherub"
Quantity: LE-10,000
Style Number: #DC111/5111
Issued: 1992
Retired: 1992

Name: "Cherub"
Quantity: LE-10,000
Style Number: #DC112/5112
Issued: 1992
Retired: 1993

Name: "The Flying Lesson"
Quantity: LE-10,000
Style Number: #DC251
Issued: 1993
Retired: 1993

Name: "Teeter Tots"
Quantity: LE-10,000
Style Number: #DC252
Issued: 1993
Retired: 1993

Name: "By The Silvery Moon"
Quantity: LE-10,000
Style Number: #DC253
Issued: 1994
Retired: 1994

Name: "The Recital"
Quantity: LE-10,000
Style Number: #DC254
Issued: 1994
Retired: 1994

Name: "Picture Perfect"
Quantity: LE-10,000
Style Number: #DC255
Issued: 1995
Retired: 1995

COLLECTOR'S
VALUE GUIDE™

Name: "The Dedication"
Quantity: LE-10,000
Style Number: #HC351/DC351
Issued: 1995
Retired: 1995

Name: "A Child Is Born"
Quantity: LE-10,000
Style Number: #DC256
Issued: 1996
Retired: 1996

Name: "Heaven's Gate"
Quantity: LE-15,000
Style Number: #DC257
Issued: 1996
Retired: 1996

Name: "Happy Landings"
Quantity: LE-5,000
Style Number: #10156
Issued: 1997
Retired: 1997

Name: "Sleigh Bells Ring"
Quantity: LE-2,500
Style Number: #10187
Issued: 1997
Retired: 1997

Name: "Cutie Pie"
Quantity: LE-12,500
Style Number: #10241
Issued: 1997
Retired: Current

Name: "Handmade With Love"
Quantity: LE-10,000
Style Number: #10324
Issued: 1998
Retired: Current

COLLECTOR'S
VALUE GUIDE™

Christmas Limited Editions

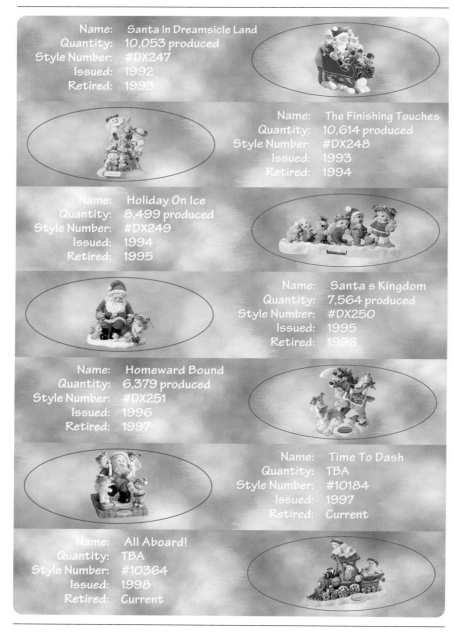

Name: Santa In Dreamsicle Land
Quantity: 10,053 produced
Style Number: #DX247
Issued: 1992
Retired: 1993

Name: The Finishing Touches
Quantity: 10,614 produced
Style Number: #DX248
Issued: 1993
Retired: 1994

Name: Holiday On Ice
Quantity: 8,499 produced
Style Number: #DX249
Issued: 1994
Retired: 1995

Name: Santa's Kingdom
Quantity: 7,564 produced
Style Number: #DX250
Issued: 1995
Retired: 1996

Name: Homeward Bound
Quantity: 6,379 produced
Style Number: #DX251
Issued: 1996
Retired: 1997

Name: Time To Dash
Quantity: TBA
Style Number: #10184
Issued: 1997
Retired: Current

Name: All Aboard!
Quantity: TBA
Style Number: #10364
Issued: 1998
Retired: Current

COLLECTOR'S
VALUE GUIDE™

Dreamsicles Top Five

This section highlights the five most valuable Dreamsicles pieces as determined by their secondary market value.

#1 Bundles Of Love (#HC370) – $1400

Topping off the *Dreamsicles Top Five* is this *Heavenly Classics* figurine, issued and suspended in 1996. It features a classical female angel soaring upwards with two little cherubs. One cherub has grabbed a teddy bear and is holding the angel's hand, the other is nestled in the crook of her arm.

#2 The Flying Lesson (#DC251) – $1000

A nervous cherub prepares to take that first leap as another cherub offers tips from a how-to manual on the art of flying, and a third offers encouragement. This *Limited Edition* figurine has flown straight up in value on the secondary market since its issue in 1993.

#3 By The Silvery Moon (#DC253) – $300

This 1993 *Limited Edition* depicts cherubs fishing from the heavens. One cherub reels in a lucky star, a second reaches in and plucks one from the cloud below, while a third cherub has the misfortune of hooking an old boot.

#4 Santa In Dreamsicle Land (#DX247) – $295

Hang on to your hats as a cherub and some animal friends get ready to take a ride among the stars with Santa in his sleigh. The first edition of the annual *Christmas Limited Editions*, this figurine was produced in 1992.

#5 Teeter Tots (#DC252) – $250

With an animal friend striving to hang on, two cherubs and a cute little bunny laugh and play on a teeter-totter in the clouds, in this 1993 *Limited Edition*.

How To Use Your Value Guide

How To Use Your Value Guide

This section features the entire Dreamsicles collection. The Value Guide begins with a chronological listing of *Dreamsicles Club Figurines*, *Limited Editions*, *Christmas Limited Editions* and *Dreamsicles Day Figurines*. Following these special sections are alphabetical listings of *Cherubs*, *Holiday Cherubs*, *Heavenly Classics*, *Dreamsicles Kids* and *Animals* (broken down by category, ie., bears, bunnies, etc.). The Value Guide concludes with other Dreamsicles collectibles, such as musicals, waterglobes, ornaments and more. If you only know the item numbers of your pieces, refer to the numerical index beginning on page 148. You can also use the alphabetical index, which begins on page 153.

How To Total The Value Of Your Collection

1. First, find your Dreamsicles piece in the Value Guide. Each piece is listed with its name, style number, size (height, unless otherwise noted), issue year and status (retired/suspended/current). In the cases where this style number has been changed, the original number is listed in parentheses immediately following the current style number. Pieces that were retired or suspended at the end of 1997 by Cast Art are listed as "Ret./Susp.: 1997" because the official status was not determined at the time of this printing. Check your local retailer for details.

A Star Is Born
CD001 • 4"
Issued: 1993 • Retired: 1993
Price Paid: $____
Market Value: $120

2. Next, write the price you originally paid for your piece on the line provided (Dreamsicles retail prices can vary). Then, write this same amount in the "Price Paid" column at the bottom of the page.

3. Record the listed "Market Value" for your piece in the "Value of My Collection" column in the bottom corner of the page. For current pieces or those which do not have an established secondary market value, fill in the amount you originally paid for the piece.

4. You can then total the columns at the bottom of the page (use a pencil so you can change totals as your collection grows) and transfer each subtotal to the chart at the end of this section to determine the total value of your collection.

COLLECTOR'S
VALUE GUIDE™

1 1993

A Star Is Born
CD001 • 4"
Issued: 1993 • Retired: 1993
Price Paid: $____
Market Value: $120

2 1994

Join The Fun
CD002 • 3"
Issued: 1994 • Retired: 1994
Price Paid: $____
Market Value: $45

3 1995

Three Cheers
CD003 • 4 ½"
Issued: 1995 • Retired: 1995
Price Paid: $____
Market Value: $55

4 1996

Star Shower
CD004 • 4 ⅛"
Issued: 1996 • Retired: 1996
Price Paid: $____
Market Value: $40

5 1997

Free Spirit
CD005 • 4"
Issued: 1997 • Retired: 1997
Price Paid: $____
Market Value: $38

6 1998

Let's Get Together
CD006 • 3 ¾"
Issued: 1998 • Current
Price Paid: $____
Market Value: $____

7 1994

Daydream Believer
CD100 • 4 ⅝"
Issued: 1994 • Retired: 1994
Price Paid: $____
Market Value: $80

8 1994

Makin' A List
CD101 • 5 ⅜"
Issued: 1994 • Retired: 1996
Price Paid: $____
Market Value: $85

9 1995

Town Crier
CD102 • 4 ½"
Issued: 1995 • Retired: 1995
Price Paid: $____
Market Value: $44

10 1995

Snowbound
CD103 • 4"
Issued: 1995 • Retired: 1996
Price Paid: $____
Market Value: $33

DREAMSICLES CLUB
SYMBOL OF MEMBERSHIP FIGURINES

	Price Paid	Value of My Collection
1.		
2.		
3.		
4.		
5.		
6.		

DREAMSICLES CLUB
MEMBERS-ONLY FIGURINES

7.		
8.		
9.		
10.		

PENCIL TOTALS

27

1 *1996*

Heavenly Flowers
CD104 • 3"
Issued: 1996 • Retired: 1997
Price Paid: $____
Market Value: $40

2 *1996*

Bee-Friended
CD105 • 4 ¼"
Issued: 1996 • Current
Price Paid: $____
Market Value: $____

3 *1997*

Peaceable Kingdom
CD106 • 2 ¼"
Issued: 1997 • Current
Price Paid: $____
Market Value: $____

4 *1997*

First Blush (LE-12,500)
CD109 • 8 ½"
Issued: 1997 • Current
Price Paid: $____
Market Value: $____

5 *1997*

Sweet Tooth
CD110 • 3 ½"
Issued: 1997 • Current
Price Paid: $____
Market Value: $____

6 *1997*

Editor's Choice
(Newsletter
Participation Gift)
CD107 • 2 ½"
Issued: 1997 • Current
Price Paid: $____
Market Value: $____

DREAMSICLES CLUB
MEMBERS-ONLY FIGURINES

	Price Paid	Value of My Collection
1.		
2.		
3.		
4.		
5.		

DREAMSICLES CLUB
SPECIAL FIGURINES

6.		
7.		

LIMITED EDITIONS

8.		
9.		
10.		

PENCIL TOTALS

7 *1997*

Golden Halo ("Good
Samaritan" Award)
CD108 • 2 ½"
Issued: 1997 • Current
Price Paid: $____
Market Value: $____

8 *1992*

Cherub (LE-10,000)
DC111 (5111) • 10"
Issued: 1992 • Retired: 1992
Price Paid: $____
Market Value: $95

9 *1992*

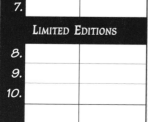

Cherub (LE-10,000)
DC112 (5112) • 10"
Issued: 1992 • Retired: 1993
Price Paid: $____
Market Value: $100

10 *1993*

The Flying Lesson
(LE-10,000)
DC251 • 13" wide
Issued: 1993 • Retired: 1993
Price Paid: $____
Market Value: $1,000

1 1993

Teeter Tots (LE-10,000)
DC252 • 6"
Issued: 1993 • Retired: 1993
Price Paid: $____
Market Value: $250

2 1994

By The Silvery Moon
(LE-10,000)
DC253 • 8 ½"
Issued: 1994 • Retired: 1994
Price Paid: $____
Market Value: $300

3 1994

The Recital (LE-10,000)
DC254 • 9 ½" wide
Issued: 1994 • Retired: 1994
Price Paid: $____
Market Value: $240

4 1995

Picture Perfect
(LE-10,000)
DC255 • 7"
Issued: 1995 • Retired: 1995
Price Paid: $____
Market Value: $130

5 1995

The Dedication
(LE-10,000)
HC351 (DC351) • 7 ½"
Issued: 1995 • Retired: 1995
Price Paid: $____
Market Value: $165

6 1996

A Child Is Born
(LE-10,000)
DC256 • 9 ½"
Issued: 1996 • Retired: 1996
Price Paid: $____
Market Value: $120

7 1996

Heaven's Gate
(LE-15,000, 5th
Anniversary Figurine)
DC257 • 8 ¾"
Issued: 1996 • Retired: 1996
Price Paid: $____
Market Value: $150

8 1997

Happy Landings
(LE-5,000)
10156 • 7 ½"
Issued: 1997 • Retired: 1997
Price Paid: $____
Market Value: $____

9 1997

Sleigh Bells Ring
(LE-2,500)
10187 • 7"
Issued: 1997 • Retired: 1997
Price Paid: $____
Market Value: $____

10 1997

Cutie Pie
(LE-12,500)
10241 • 8"
Issued: 1997 • Current
Price Paid: $____
Market Value: $____

LIMITED EDITIONS		
	Price Paid	Value of My Collection
1.		
2.		
3.		
4.		
5.		
6.		
7.		
8.		
9.		
10.		
PENCIL TOTALS		

1 *1998*

Handmade With Love
(LE-10,000)
10324 • 5″
Issued: 1998 • Current
Price Paid: $____
Market Value: $_____

2 *1992*

Santa In Dreamsicle Land
DX247 • 10″
Issued: 1992 • Retired: 1993
Price Paid: $____
Market Value: $295

3 *1993*

The Finishing Touches
DX248 • 9″
Issued: 1993 • Retired: 1994
Price Paid: $____
Market Value: $165

4 *1994*

Holiday On Ice
DX249 • 8 ½″
Issued: 1994 • Retired: 1995
Price Paid: $____
Market Value: $140

5 *1995*

Santa's Kingdom
DX250 • 8 ½″ wide
Issued: 1995 • Retired: 1996
Price Paid: $____
Market Value: $110

6 *1996*

Homeward Bound
DX251 • 9″
Issued: 1996 • Retired: 1997
Price Paid: $____
Market Value: $100

LIMITED EDITIONS

	Price Paid	Value of My Collection
1.		

CHRISTMAS LIMITED EDITIONS

2.		
3.		
4.		
5.		
6.		
7.		
8.		

DREAMSICLES DAY FIGURINES

9.		
10.		

PENCIL TOTALS

7 *1997*

Time To Dash
10184 • 6 ¾″
Issued: 1997 • Current
Price Paid: $____
Market Value: $85

8 *1998*

All Aboard!
10364 • 7″
Issued: 1998 • Current
Price Paid: $____
Market Value: $_____

9 *1995*

1995 Dreamsicles Day Event Figurine
DC075 • 3 ½″
Issued: 1995 • Retired: 1995
Price Paid: $____
Market Value: $55

10 *1996*

Glad Tidings
DD100 • 4 ⅛″
Issued: 1996 • Retired: 1996
Price Paid: $____
Market Value: $50

1 1996

Time To Retire
DD103 • 4 ⅛"
Issued: 1996 • Retired: 1997
Price Paid: $____
Market Value: $28

2 1997

The Golden Rule
E9701 • 4 ⅜"
Issued: 1997 • Retired: 1997
Price Paid: $____
Market Value: $45

3 1998

A Day Of Fun
E9801 • 4"
Issued: 1998 • Current
Price Paid: $____
Market Value: $____

4 New

1001 Baby Names
10358 • 5 ½"
Issued: 1998 • Current
Price Paid: $____
Market Value: $____

5

All Better Now
DC246 • 2 ¾"
Issued: 1995 • Ret./Susp.: 1997
Price Paid: $____
Market Value: $____

6

All My Lovin'
DC313 • 3 ¼"
Issued: 1996 • Current
Price Paid: $____
Market Value: $____

7

All Star
10165 • 4"
Issued: 1997 • Current
Price Paid: $____
Market Value: $____

8

Among Friends (June)
DC185 • 3 ¾"
Issued: 1994 • Retired: 1995
Price Paid: $____
Market Value: $55

9

Autumn Leaves (October)
DC189 • 5"
Issued: 1994 • Retired: 1995
Price Paid: $____
Market Value: $55

10

Baby And Me
DC054 • 3"
Issued: 1994 • Ret./Susp.: 1997
Price Paid: $____
Market Value: $____

DREAMSICLES DAY FIGURINES

	Price Paid	Value of My Collection
1.		
2.		
3.		

CHERUBS

4.		
5.		
6.		
7.		
8.		
9.		
10.		

PENCIL TOTALS

1

Baby Boom
10045 • 3 ½″
Issued: 1997 • Current
Price Paid: $____
Market Value: $____

2

Baby Boom
10139 • 3 ½″
Issued: 1997 • Current
Price Paid: $____
Market Value: $____

3

Baby Kisses
DC080 • 2 ½″
Issued: 1995 • Current
Price Paid: $____
Market Value: $____

4

Baby Love
DC147 • 2 ½″
Issued: 1992 • Retired: 1995
Price Paid: $____
Market Value: $15

5

Baby Steps
DC415 • 3 ⅝″
Issued: 1996 • Ret./Susp.: 1997
Price Paid: $____
Market Value: $____

6

Back Packin'
DC346 • 4 ¼″
Issued: 1996 • Current
Price Paid: $____
Market Value: $____

CHERUBS

	Price Paid	Value of My Collection
1.		
2.		
3.		
4.		
5.		
6.		
7.		
8.		
9.		
10.		

PENCIL TOTALS

7 New

Baked With Love
10262 • 4″
Issued: 1998 • Current
Price Paid: $____
Market Value: $____

8 New

The Baptism
10321 • 2 ¾″
Issued: 1998 • Current
Price Paid: $____
Market Value: $____

9

Bar Mitzvah Boy
DC408 • 4″
Issued: 1995 • Ret./Susp.: 1997
Price Paid: $____
Market Value: $____

10

Bashful
10031 • 4″
Issued: 1997 • Current
Price Paid: $____
Market Value: $____

①

Bedtime Prayer
DC703 • 3"
Issued: 1995 • Current
Price Paid: $____
Market Value: $_____

②

Berry Cute
DC109 • 3 ⅞"
Issued: 1996 • Current
Price Paid: $____
Market Value: $_____

③

Best Buddies
DC159 • 3 ¾"
Issued: 1995 • Current
Price Paid: $____
Market Value: $_____

④

Best Friends
DC342 • 6"
Issued: 1996 • Current
Price Paid: $____
Market Value: $_____

⑤

Best Pals
DC103 (5103) • 4 ¾"
Issued: 1991 • Retired: 1994
Price Paid: $____
Market Value: $45

⑥

Bird In Hand
10129 • 3 ½"
Issued: 1997 • Current
Price Paid: $____
Market Value: $_____

⑦

Birdie And Me
DC056 • 2 ½"
Issued: 1994 • Ret./Susp.: 1997
Price Paid: $____
Market Value: $_____

⑧ New

Birthday Fun
10323 • 3 ¾"
Issued: 1998 • Current
Price Paid: $____
Market Value: $_____

⑨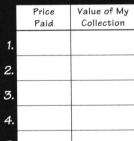

Birthday Party
DC171 • 4 ½
Issued: 1994 • Suspended: 1995
Price Paid: $____
Market Value: $_____

⑩

Birthday Wishes
10166 • 3 ¼"
Issued: 1997 • Current
Price Paid: $____
Market Value: $_____

CHERUBS

	Price Paid	Value of My Collection
1.		
2.		
3.		
4.		
5.		
6.		
7.		
8.		
9.		
10.		
PENCIL TOTALS		

①

Bless This Meal
10064 • 2 ¾"
Issued: 1997 • Current
Price Paid: $____
Market Value: $_____

②

Bless Us All
DC089 • 2 ⅝"
Issued: 1995 • Current
Price Paid: $____
Market Value: $_____

③ *New*

Blocks Of Love
10264 • 3 ¾"
Issued: 1998 • Current
Price Paid: $____
Market Value: $_____

④

Blowing Bubbles
(Parade Of Gifts
Exclusive)
10115 • 3 ⅝"
Issued: 1997 • Current
Price Paid: $____
Market Value: $_____

⑤

Blue Logo Sculpture
DC002 • 6 ½" wide
Issued: 1992 • Retired: 1994
Price Paid: $____
Market Value: $50

⑥

Bluebird On My
Shoulder
DC115 • 6"
Issued: 1992 • Retired: 1995
Price Paid: $____
Market Value: $30

CHERUBS

	Price Paid	Value of My Collection
1.		
2.		
3.		
4.		
5.		
6.		
7.		
8.		
9.		
10.		
PENCIL TOTALS		

⑦

Born This Day
DC230 • 4"
Issued: 1994 • Ret./Susp.: 1997
Price Paid: $____
Market Value: $_____

⑧

Boxful Of Stars
DC224 • 3 ¾"
Issued: 1994 • Suspended: 1995
Price Paid: $____
Market Value: $_____

⑨

Bright Eyes
DC108 (5108) • 3 ½"
Issued: 1991 • Current
Price Paid: $____
Market Value: $_____

⑩

Brotherhood
DC307 • 4 ½"
Issued: 1995 • Current
Price Paid: $____
Market Value: $_____

① 	② 	③ 
Brown Baggin' **DC716 • 3"** Issued: 1996 • Ret./Susp.: 1997 Price Paid: $____ *Market Value: $____*	**Bubble Bath** **DC416 • 5"** Issued: 1996 • Current Price Paid: $____ *Market Value: $____*	**Bundle Of Joy** **DC142 • 2 ½"** Issued: 1992 • Retired: 1995 Price Paid: $____ *Market Value: $14*
④ 	⑤ 	⑥ 
Bunny And Me **DC055 • 2 ⅝"** Issued: 1994 • Ret./Susp.: 1997 Price Paid: $____ *Market Value: $____*	**Bunny Love** **(GCC Exclusive)** **10062 • 3 ½"** Issued: 1997 • Current Price Paid: $____ *Market Value: $____*	**Bunny Mine** **10068 • 3 ⅜"** Issued: 1997 • Current Price Paid: $____ *Market Value: $____*

⑦ New 	⑧ 
Bunny Pal **10342 • 2 ½"** Issued: 1998 • Current Price Paid: $____ *Market Value: $____*	**Bunny Power** **10067 • 4"** Issued: 1997 • Current Price Paid: $____ *Market Value: $____*
⑨	⑩ 
Burning Love **DC220 • 5"** Issued: 1995 • Ret./Susp.: 1997 Price Paid: $____ *Market Value: $____*	**Caroler #1** **DC216 • 6 ½"** Issued: 1992 • Retired: 1995 Price Paid: $____ *Market Value: $38*

CHERUBS

	Price Paid	Value of My Collection
1.		
2.		
3.		
4.		
5.		
6.		
7.		
8.		
9.		
10.		

✎ **PENCIL TOTALS**

(1)
Caroler #2
DC217 • 6 ½"
Issued: 1992 • Retired: 1995
Price Paid: $_____
Market Value: $38

(2)
Caroler #3
DC218 • 6 ½"
Issued: 1992 • Retired: 1995
Price Paid: $_____
Market Value: $38

(3)
Carousel
DC174 • 7"
Issued: 1994 • Suspended: 1996
Price Paid: $_____
Market Value: $45

(4)
Catch A Falling Star
DC166 • 4 ½"
Issued: 1993 • Retired: 1997
Price Paid: $_____
Market Value: $16

(5)
Charity
10171 • 2 ⅜"
Issued: 1997 • Current
Price Paid: $_____
Market Value: $_____

(6)
Chatter Box
10039 • 3 ½"
Issued: 1997 • Current
Price Paid: $_____
Market Value: $_____

CHERUBS		
	Price Paid	Value of My Collection
1.		
2.		
3.		
4.		
5.		
6.		
7.		
8.		
9.		
10.		
PENCIL TOTALS		

(7)
Cherub And Child
DC100 (5100) • 5 ½"
Issued: 1991 • Retired: 1995
Price Paid: $_____
Market Value: $42

(8)
Cherub For All Seasons
(set/4)
DC114 (5114) • 8"
Issued: 1992 • Retired: 1995
Price Paid: $_____
Market Value: $70

(9)
A Child's Prayer
DC145 • 2 ½"
Issued: 1992 • Retired: 1995
Price Paid: $_____
Market Value: $15

(10)
A Child's Prayer
DC405 • 4"
Issued: 1995 • Current
Price Paid: $_____
Market Value: $_____

1

The Christening
DC300 • 4 ¾″
Issued: 1995 • Ret./Susp.: 1997
Price Paid: $____
Market Value: $____

2

Come To Papa
DC088 • 2 ¼″
Issued: 1995 • Current
Price Paid: $____
Market Value: $____

3

Corona Centennial
N/A • 3″
Issued: 1996 • Retired: 1996
Price Paid: $____
Market Value: $210

4

Costume Party
10205 • 3 ¾″
Issued: 1997 • Current
Price Paid: $____
Market Value: $____

5

Counting Sheep
DC417 • 5″
Issued: 1996 • Current
Price Paid: $____
Market Value: $____

6

New

Cow Pal
10335 • 2 ½″
Issued: 1998 • Current
Price Paid: $____
Market Value: $____

7

Crossing Guardian
DC422 • 5″
Issued: 1996 • Current
Price Paid: $____
Market Value: $____

8

Cuddle Blanket
DC153 • 2″
Issued: 1994 • Retired: 1995
Price Paid: $____
Market Value: $14

9

Cuddle Up
DC324 • 2 ¼″
Issued: 1996 • Current
Price Paid: $____
Market Value: $____

10

Cupid's Arrow
DC199 • 5 ¼″
Issued: 1994 • Ret./Susp.: 1997
Price Paid: $____
Market Value: $____

	Price Paid	Value of My Collection
CHERUBS		
1.		
2.		
3.		
4.		
5.		
6.		
7.		
8.		
9.		
10.		
PENCIL TOTALS		

①

Cupid's Bow
DC202 (5133) • 7 ½"
Issued: 1992 • Suspended: 1993
Price Paid: $____
Market Value: $80

②

Cut-Out Cutie (Parade Of Gifts Exclusive)
10097 • 4"
Issued: 1997 • Current
Price Paid: $____
Market Value: $____

③

Daffodil Days (American Cancer Society Figurine)
DC343 • 3 ½"
Issued: 1996 • Retired 1997
Price Paid: $____
Market Value: $____

④ New

Daydreamin'
10332 • 6 ½"
Issued: 1998 • Current
Price Paid: $____
Market Value: $____

⑤

Dear Diary
10162 • 2 ¼"
Issued: 1997 • Current
Price Paid: $____
Market Value: $____

⑥ New

Doggie Pal
10340 • 2 ¼"
Issued: 1998 • Current
Price Paid: $____
Market Value: $____

CHERUBS		
	Price Paid	Value of My Collection
1.		
2.		
3.		
4.		
5.		
6.		
7.		
8.		
9.		
10.		
PENCIL TOTALS		

⑦

Don't Rock The Boat
DC404 • 5 ½"
Issued: 1995 • Ret./Susp.: 1997
Price Paid: $____
Market Value: $____

⑧

Double Dip
DC349 • 5"
Issued: 1996 • Current
Price Paid: $____
Market Value: $____

⑨

Dream A Little Dream
DC144 • 2 ½"
Issued: 1992 • Retired: 1995
Price Paid: $____
Market Value: $15

⑩

Dream, Dream, Dream (Early Release - Fall 1997)
10247 • 2 ⅞"
Issued: TBA • Current
Price Paid: $____
Market Value: $____

1 New

Dream On
10365 • 4 ¾"
Issued: 1998 • Current
Price Paid: $____
Market Value: $____

2

Dream Weaver
10159 • 3 ⅝"
Issued: 1997 • Current
Price Paid: $____
Market Value: $____

3

Dreamin' Of You
10030 • 3 ⅛"
Issued: 1997 • Current
Price Paid: $____
Market Value: $____

4

Dreidel, Dreidel
DC302 • 2 ⅝"
Issued: 1995 • Ret./Susp.: 1997
Price Paid: $____
Market Value: $____

5 New

Duckie Pal
10341 • 2 ⅜"
Issued: 1998 • Current
Price Paid: $____
Market Value: $____

6

Eager To Please
DC154 • 2"
Issued: 1994 • Retired: 1995
Price Paid: $____
Market Value: $15

7 New

Easter Artist
10325 • 3 ¾"
Issued: 1998 • Current
Price Paid: $____
Market Value: $____

8 New

Easter Basket
10322 • 3"
Issued: 1998 • Current
Price Paid: $____
Market Value: $____

9

Easter Morning
DC312 • 2 ⅞"
Issued: 1996 • Current
Price Paid: $____
Market Value: $____

10

Easy Rider
DC414 • 3 ¾"
Issued: 1996 • Ret./Susp.: 1997
Price Paid: $____
Market Value: $____

CHERUBS		
	Price Paid	Value of My Collection
1.		
2.		
3.		
4.		
5.		
6.		
7.		
8.		
9.		
10.		
PENCIL TOTALS		

①

Eggstra Special
10063 • 3 ⁵/₈"
Issued: 1997 • Current
Price Paid: $____
Market Value: $____

② New

Elephant Pal
10344 • 2 ³/₈"
Issued: 1998 • Current
Price Paid: $____
Market Value: $____

③

Feet First
DC320 • 3 ¼"
Issued: 1996 • Ret./Susp.: 1997
Price Paid: $____
Market Value: $____

④

Felicity
10174 • 2 ½"
Issued: 1997 • Current
Price Paid: $____
Market Value: $____

⑤

Finger Food
DC083 • 2 ¼"
Issued: 1995 • Current
Price Paid: $____
Market Value: $____

⑥

First Born
10130 • 4 ³/₈"
Issued: 1997 • Current
Price Paid: $____
Market Value: $____

CHERUBS

	Price Paid	Value of My Collection
1.		
2.		
3.		
4.		
5.		
6.		
7.		
8.		
9.		
10.		

PENCIL TOTALS

⑦

First Communion
DC301 • 3 ¾"
Issued: 1995 • Ret./Susp.: 1997
Price Paid: $____
Market Value: $____

⑧

Follow Me
10050 • 4 ¼"
Issued: 1997 • Current
Price Paid: $____
Market Value: $____

⑨

Forever Friends
DC102 (5102) • 4 ½"
Issued: 1991 • Retired: 1994
Price Paid: $____
Market Value: $45

⑩ New

Forever Friends
(Dreamsicles Expressions)
10276 • 3 ¾"
Issued: 1998 • Current
Price Paid: $____
Market Value: $____

(1)

Forever Yours
DC110 (5110) • 10"
Issued: 1991 • Retired: 1995
Price Paid: $____
Market Value: $65

(2)

Forget Me Not
DC325 • 2 ¼"
Issued: 1996 • Current
Price Paid: $____
Market Value: $____

(3)

Forty Winks
DC233 • 3 ½"
Issued: 1995 • Ret./Susp.: 1997
Price Paid: $____
Market Value: $____

(4)

Fountain Treat
(Early Release - Fall 1997)
10244 • 5"
Issued: TBA • Current
Price Paid: $____
Market Value: $____

(5)

Free Bird
DC234 • 3 ¾"
Issued: 1995 • Ret./Susp.: 1997
Price Paid: $____
Market Value: $____

(6)

Friendship Cherubs
(set/2)
DC175 • 2"
Issued: 1994 • Current
Price Paid: $____
Market Value: $____

(7)

From The Heart
10116 • 2 ½"
Issued: 1997 • Current
Price Paid: $____
Market Value: $____

(8)

Gecko Guava
10005 • 3 ⅝"
Issued: 1996 • Retired: 1997
Price Paid: $____
Market Value: $____

(9)

Get Better Soon
DC245 • 3"
Issued: 1995 • Ret./Susp.: 1997
Price Paid: $____
Market Value: $____

(10)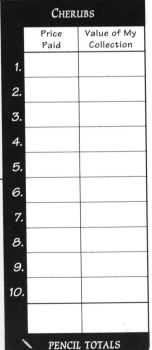

Get Well Soon
DC244 • 4"
Issued: 1995 • Retired: 1997
Price Paid: $____
Market Value: $____

CHERUBS

	Price Paid	Value of My Collection
1.		
2.		
3.		
4.		
5.		
6.		
7.		
8.		
9.		
10.		
PENCIL TOTALS		

① New

Get Well Wishes
10320 • 2 ⅞"
Issued: 1998 • Current
Price Paid: $____
Market Value: $_____

②

Go For The Gold
DC315 • 3 ⅞"
Issued: 1996 • Current
Price Paid: $____
Market Value: $_____

③

God Bless America
DC706 • 3 ½"
Issued: 1995 • Ret./Susp.: 1997
Price Paid: $____
Market Value: $_____

④

God's Word
10157 • 3 ⅜"
Issued: 1997 • Current
Price Paid: $____
Market Value: $_____

⑤

The Good Book
DC361 • 3 ⅜"
Issued: 1997 • Current
Price Paid: $____
Market Value: $_____

⑥

Good Shepherd
DC104 • 4"
Issued: 1994 • Suspended: 1996
Price Paid: $____
Market Value: $_____

CHERUBS		
	Price Paid	Value of My Collection
1.		
2.		
3.		
4.		
5.		
6.		
7.		
8.		
9.		
10.		
PENCIL TOTALS		

⑦

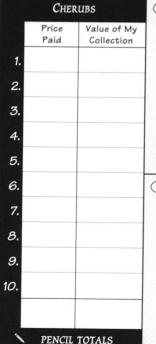

Goodness Me
10160 • 2 ⅞"
Issued: 1997 • Current
Price Paid: $____
Market Value: $_____

⑧

The Graduate
DC135 • 5"
Issued: 1994 • Current
Price Paid: $____
Market Value: $_____

⑨

Graduation Day
DC219 • 4 ¼"
Issued: 1995 • Current
Price Paid: $____
Market Value: $_____

⑩

Grand Old Flag
DC232 • 3"
Issued: 1995 • Ret./Susp.: 1997
Price Paid: $____
Market Value: $_____

1 New

Grandma I Love You
(Dreamsicles Expressions)
10273 • 3 ¾"
Issued: 1998 • Current
Price Paid: $____
Market Value: $____

2

Grandma's Or Bust
DC227 • 4"
Issued: 1995 • Current
Price Paid: $____
Market Value: $____

3

Granny's Cookies
DC228 • 2 ½"
Issued: 1995 • **Current**
Price Paid: $____
Market Value: $____

4

Haley
DC321 • 4"
Issued: 1996 • Ret./Susp.: 1997
Price Paid: $____
Market Value: $____

5

Hand In Hand
DC431 • 3 ½"
Issued: 1997 • Current
Price Paid: $____
Market Value: $____

6

Handful Of Hearts
DC204 • 3 ½"
Issued: 1993 • Current
Price Paid: $____
Market Value: $____

7

Hang Loose
10004 • 3 ⅝"
Issued: 1996 • Ret./Susp.: 1997
Price Paid: $____
Market Value: $____

8

Happy Birthday Cherub
DC133 • 4"
Issued: 1994 • Suspended: 1995
Price Paid: $____
Market Value: $17

9

The Happy Couple
10219 • 6 ¼"
Issued: 1997 • Current
Price Paid: $____
Market Value: $____

10

Happy Feet
DC164 • 3"
Issued: 1995 • Current
Price Paid: $____
Market Value: $____

	CHERUBS	
	Price Paid	Value of My Collection
1.		
2.		
3.		
4.		
5.		
6.		
7.		
8.		
9.		
10.		
	PENCIL TOTALS	

Dreamsicles™ — Value Guide

1

Happy Graduate
DC705 • 4 ¼"
Issued: 1995 • Current
Price Paid: $____
Market Value: $____

2

Happy Heart
DC211 • 2 ⅞"
Issued: 1995 • Current
Price Paid: $____
Market Value: $____

3

Have A Heart
DC198 • 3 ¼"
Issued: 1994 • Ret./Susp.: 1997
Price Paid: $____
Market Value: $____

4

Hawaiian Love Song
10003 • 5"
Issued: 1996 • Ret./Susp.: 1997
Price Paid: $____
Market Value: $____

5

Hear No Evil
10040 • 5 ½"
Issued: 1997 • Current
Price Paid: $____
Market Value: $____

6

Hear No Evil, See No Evil, Speak No Evil (set/3)
10098 • various
Issued: 1997 • Current
Price Paid: $____
Market Value: $____

CHERUBS		
	Price Paid	Value of My Collection
1.		
2.		
3.		
4.		
5.		
6.		
7.		
8.		
9.		
10.		
PENCIL TOTALS		

7
New

Heart On A String
10261 • 2 ½"
Issued: 1998 • Current
Price Paid: $____
Market Value: $____

8

Heart Throb
DC193 • 2 ¾"
Issued: 1995 • Current
Price Paid: $____
Market Value: $____

9

Heart's Desire
DC090 • 2 ½"
Issued: 1995 • Current
Price Paid: $____
Market Value: $____

10

Hearts And Flowers
DC433 • 3 ½"
Issued: 1997 • Current
Price Paid: $____
Market Value: $____

1

Heartstrings
DC197 • 2 ½"
Issued: 1994 • Current
Price Paid: $____
Market Value: $____

2

Heavenly Dreamer
DC106 (5106) • 5 ½"
Issued: 1991 • Retired: 1996
Price Paid: $____
Market Value: $15

3

Hello Dolly
DC702 • 3 ½"
Issued: 1995 • Ret./Susp.: 1997
Price Paid: $____
Market Value: $____

4

Here's Looking At You
DC172 • 4"
Issued: 1994 • Retired: 1995
Price Paid: $____
Market Value: $____

5

Here's My Hand
10248 • 4 ¼"
Issued: 1997 • Current
Price Paid: $____
Market Value: $____

6 *New*

Here's My Heart
10260 • 2 ½"
Issued: 1998 • Current
Price Paid: $____
Market Value: $____

7 *New*

Hey Diddle Diddle
10373 • 5"
Issued: 1998 • Current
Price Paid: $____
Market Value: $____

8

Hold Tight
(Cracker Barrel Exclusive)
DC018 • 3 ⅝"
Issued: 1996 • Current
Price Paid: $____
Market Value: $____

9

Holiday Magic
(December)
DC191 • 5"
Issued: 1994 • Retired: 1995
Price Paid: $____
Market Value: $55

10 *New*

Home Sweet Home
10381 • 3 ¾"
Issued: 1998 • Current
Price Paid: $____
Market Value: $____

CHERUBS		
	Price Paid	Value of My Collection
1.		
2.		
3.		
4.		
5.		
6.		
7.		
8.		
9.		
10.		
PENCIL TOTALS		

1

Hugabye Baby
DC701 • 3"
Issued: 1995 • Retired: 1997
Price Paid: $____
Market Value: $____

2

Huge Hugs
10181 • 4 ½"
Issued: 1997 • Current
Price Paid: $____
Market Value: $____

3

Humility
10173 • 2 ⅝"
Issued: 1997 • Current
Price Paid: $____
Market Value: $____

4 New

Humpty Dumpty
10372 • 4 ¼"
Issued: 1998 • Current
Price Paid: $____
Market Value: $____

5

Hushaby Baby
DC303 • 3 ¾"
Issued: 1995 • Suspended: 1996
Price Paid: $____
Market Value: $____

6

I.C.E. Figurine
(LE-2,300, I.C.E. Exclusive)
SP001 • 6"
Issued: 1994 • Retired: 1995
Price Paid: $____
Market Value: $165

CHERUBS

	Price Paid	Value of My Collection
1.		
2.		
3.		
4.		
5.		
6.		
7.		
8.		
9.		
10.		
PENCIL TOTALS		

7

I Can Read
DC151 • 2"
Issued: 1994 • Retired: 1995
Price Paid: $____
Market Value: $14

8

I Love Mommy
DC226 • 2 ¾"
Issued: 1995 • Current
Price Paid: $____
Market Value: $____

9

I Love You
DC225 • 4 ½"
Issued: 1995 • Current
Price Paid: $____
Market Value: $____

10 New

I Love You
(Dreamsicles Expressions)
10271 • 3 ¾"
Issued: 1998 • Current
Price Paid: $____
Market Value: $____

CHERUBS

① New

Ice Dancing
(Early Release - Fall 1997)
10256 • 4"
Issued: 1998 • Current
Price Paid: $____
Market Value: $_____

②

Integrity
10175 • 2 ⅛"
Issued: 1997 • Current
Price Paid: $____
Market Value: $_____

③

Intervention
DC425 • 3 ¾"
Issued: 1996 • Current
Price Paid: $____
Market Value: $_____

④

Irish Eyes
DC322 • 2 ⅞"
Issued: 1996 • Current
Price Paid: $____
Market Value: $_____

⑤

It's Your Birthday
DC304 • 2 ⅞"
Issued: 1995 • Current
Price Paid: $____
Market Value: $_____

⑥

It's Your Day
10220 • 5"
Issued: 1997 • Current
Price Paid: $____
Market Value: $_____

⑦

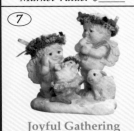

Joyful Gathering
DC231 • 5"
Issued: 1994 • Ret./Susp.: 1997
Price Paid: $____
Market Value: $_____

⑧

Joyful Noise
DC409 • 3 ⅞"
Issued: 1996 • Ret./Susp.: 1997
Price Paid: $____
Market Value: $_____

CHERUBS

	Price Paid	Value of My Collection
1.		
2.		
3.		
4.		
5.		
6.		
7.		
8.		
9.		
10.		

PENCIL TOTALS

⑨ New

Jumping Jack
10374 • 4"
Issued: 1998 • Current
Price Paid: $____
Market Value: $_____

⑩

King Of The Jungle
10183 • 4 ¼"
Issued: 1997 • Current
Price Paid: $____
Market Value: $_____

①

A Kiss For Momma
DC402 • 3"
Issued: 1995 • Current
Price Paid: $____
Market Value: $_____

②

A Kiss In Time
DC309 • 4"
Issued: 1995 • Ret./Susp.: 1997
Price Paid: $____
Market Value: $_____

③

Kiss, Kiss
DC213 • 2"
Issued: 1995 • Current
Price Paid: $____
Market Value: $_____

④

Kitty And Me
DC051 • 3"
Issued: 1994 • Ret./Susp.: 1997
Price Paid: $____
Market Value: $_____

⑤ *New*

Kitty Pal
10343 • 2 ⅜"
Issued: 1998 • Current
Price Paid: $____
Market Value: $_____

⑥ *New*

Lambie Pal
10336 • 2 ⅜"
Issued: 1998 • Current
Price Paid: $____
Market Value: $_____

CHERUBS

	Price Paid	Value of My Collection
1.		
2.		
3.		
4.		
5.		
6.		
7.		
8.		
9.		
10.		

PENCIL TOTALS

⑦

Land Ho!
10043 • 3"
Issued: 1997 • Current
Price Paid: $____
Market Value: $_____

⑧

Let's Eat
(Early Release - Fall 1997)
10252 • 4"
Issued: TBA • Current
Price Paid: $____
Market Value: $_____

⑨

Let's Play Fetch
DC237 • 4 ½"
Issued: 1995 • Ret./Susp.: 1997
Price Paid: $____
Market Value: $_____

⑩

Life Is Good
DC119 • 5 ¼"
Issued: 1992 • Retired: 1996
Price Paid: $____
Market Value: $_____

1 New

Little Bo Peep
10375 • 3 ⅞"
Issued: 1998 • Current
Price Paid: $____
Market Value: $_____

2

Little Cupid
DC212 • 2"
Issued: 1995 • Current
Price Paid: $____
Market Value: $_____

3

Little Darlin'
DC146 • 2 ½"
Issued: 1992 • Retired: 1995
Price Paid: $____
Market Value: $14

4 New

Little Leaguer
10366 • 3 ⅛"
Issued: 1998 • Current
Price Paid: $____
Market Value: $_____

5

Little One
10033 • 3 ⅞"
Issued: 1997 • Current
Price Paid: $____
Market Value: $_____

6

Littlest Angel
DC143 • 2 ½"
Issued: 1992 • Retired: 1995
Price Paid: $____
Market Value: $14

7

Logo Sculpture
DC003 • 7" wide
Issued: 1995 • Current
Price Paid: $____
Market Value: $_____

8

Lots Of Love
DC403 • 3"
Issued: 1995 • Current
Price Paid: $____
Market Value: $_____

9

Love In Bloom (May)
DC184 • 5"
Issued: 1994 • Retired: 1995
Price Paid: $____
Market Value: $55

10

Love Letters
DC430 • 3 ¼"
Issued: 1997 • Current
Price Paid: $____
Market Value: $_____

CHERUBS

	Price Paid	Value of My Collection
1.		
2.		
3.		
4.		
5.		
6.		
7.		
8.		
9.		
10.		
PENCIL TOTALS		

Dreamsicles™ — Value Guide

1
Love Me Do
DC194 • 4 ¾"
Issued: 1995 • Current
Price Paid: $____
Market Value: $_____

2 *New*
Love My Bunny
10367 • 4"
Issued: 1998 • Current
Price Paid: $____
Market Value: $_____

3
Love My Kitty
DC130 • 3 ¾"
Issued: 1993 • Retired: 1997
Price Paid: $____
Market Value: $_____

4 *New*
Love My Lamb
10368 • 4 ½"
Issued: 1998 • Current
Price Paid: $____
Market Value: $_____

5
Love My Puppy
DC131 • 3 ¾"
Issued: 1993 • Retired: 1997
Price Paid: $____
Market Value: $_____

6
Love My Teddy
DC132 • 4"
Issued: 1993 • Retired: 1997
Price Paid: $____
Market Value: $_____

Cherubs

	Price Paid	Value of My Collection
1.		
2.		
3.		
4.		
5.		
6.		
7.		
8.		
9.		
10.		
PENCIL TOTALS		

7
Love To Mom
DC717 • 2 ⅜"
Issued: 1997 • Current
Price Paid: $____
Market Value: $_____

8 *New*
Love You Sew
10263 • 3"
Issued: 1998 • Current
Price Paid: $____
Market Value: $_____

9
Loverly
DC714 • 2 ⅝"
Issued: 1996 • Current
Price Paid: $____
Market Value: $_____

10
Lullaby
DC173 • 10" wide
Issued: 1994 • Ret./Susp.: 1997
Price Paid: $____
Market Value: $_____

1
Lyrical Lute
10169 • 6 ½"
Issued: 1997 • Current
Price Paid: $____
Market Value: $____

2
Make A Wish
DC118 • 5 ½"
Issued: 1992 • Current
Price Paid: $____
Market Value: $____

3
Making A Cake
DC418 • 4 ¼"
Issued: 1996 • Current
Price Paid: $____
Market Value: $____

4 New
Matchmaker
10327 • 5 ⅝"
Issued: 1998 • Current
Price Paid: $____
Market Value: $____

5
Me And My Shadow
DC116 • 5 ½"
Issued: 1993 • Retired: 1996
Price Paid: $____
Market Value: $____

6
Mellow Cello
10170 • 9 ½"
Issued: 1997 • Current
Price Paid: $____
Market Value: $____

7
Mermaid's Gift
10002 • 4"
Issued: 1996 • Ret./Susp.: 1997
Price Paid: $____
Market Value: $____

8
Mischief Maker
DC105 (5105) • 5"
Issued: 1991 • Retired: 1996
Price Paid: $____
Market Value: $____

9
Miss Morningstar
DC141 • 7 ¼"
Issued: 1993 • Retired: 1996
Price Paid: $____
Market Value: $50

10 New
Mom's Garden
10328 • 4 ½"
Issued: 1998 • Current
Price Paid: $____
Market Value: $____

CHERUBS	Price Paid	Value of My Collection
1.		
2.		
3.		
4.		
5.		
6.		
7.		
8.		
9.		
10.		
PENCIL TOTALS		

1

Mom's The Best
DC428 • 2 ⅜"
Issued: 1997 • Current
Price Paid: $____
Market Value: $____

2
New

Monkey Pal
10337 • 2 ⅝"
Issued: 1998 • Current
Price Paid: $____
Market Value: $____

3

Moon Dance
DC210 • 5 ½"
Issued: 1994 • Retired: 1997
Price Paid: $____
Market Value: $____

4

Moonglow
DC235 • 3 ¾"
Issued: 1995 • Ret./Susp.: 1997
Price Paid: $____
Market Value: $____

5
New

Moonstruck
(Early Release - Fall 1997)
10384 (10127) • 3 ⅜"
Issued: 1998 • Current
Price Paid: $____
Market Value: $____

6
New

Mother I Love You
(Dreamsicles Expressions)
10272 • 3 ¾"
Issued: 1998 • Current
Price Paid: $____
Market Value: $____

CHERUBS

	Price Paid	Value of My Collection
1.		
2.		
3.		
4.		
5.		
6.		
7.		
8.		
9.		
10.		
PENCIL TOTALS		

7

Mother-To-Be
10155 • 5 ¾"
Issued: 1997 • Current
Price Paid: $____
Market Value: $____

8
New

Mother's Helper
(Early Release - Fall 1997)
10141 • 3 ⅛"
Issued: 1998 • Current
Price Paid: $____
Market Value: $____

9
New

Music Makers
10382 • 3 ¼"
Issued: 1998 • Current
Price Paid: $____
Market Value: $____

10

My First Reader
DC087 • 3"
Issued: 1995 • Current
Price Paid: $____
Market Value: $____

1

My Funny Valentine
DC201 (5132) • 5 ½"
Issued: 1992 • Suspended: 1993
Price Paid: $____
Market Value: $55

2

My Prayer
DC121 • 5 ½"
Issued: 1992 • Current
Price Paid: $____
Market Value: $____

3

Nature's Bounty
(August)
DC187 • 4"
Issued: 1994 • Retired: 1995
Price Paid: $____
Market Value: $55

4

Newborn Cherub
DC168 • 3" wide
Issued: 1994 • Suspended: 1996
Price Paid: $____
Market Value: $____

5

'Nite 'Nite
DC238 • 4 ½"
Issued: 1995 • Ret./Susp.: 1997
Price Paid: $____
Market Value: $____

6

Northern Exposure
DC420 • 5 ½"
Issued: 1996 • Ret./Susp.: 1997
Price Paid: $____
Market Value: $____

7

Now Give Thanks
(November)
DC190 • 4 ¾"
Issued: 1994 • Retired: 1995
Price Paid: $____
Market Value: $55

8

Now I Lay Me . . .
DC406 • 4"
Issued: 1995 • Current
Price Paid: $____
Market Value: $____

9

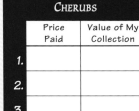

Nursery Rhyme
DC229 • 7"
Issued: 1995 • Suspended: 1995
Price Paid: $____
Market Value: $70

10

Ocean's Call
DC317 • 2 ½"
Issued: 1996 • Current
Price Paid: $____
Market Value: $____

CHERUBS

	Price Paid	Value of My Collection
1.		
2.		
3.		
4.		
5.		
6.		
7.		
8.		
9.		
10.		
PENCIL TOTALS		

Dreamsicles™ – VALUE GUIDE

1

On Bended Knee
DC196 • 2 ¼"
Issued: 1994 • Current
Price Paid: $____
Market Value: $____

2

One World
DC306 • 3 ⅞"
Issued: 1995 • Current
Price Paid: $____
Market Value: $____

3

Open Me First
DC243 • 3 ¼"
Issued: 1994 • Suspended: 1996
Price Paid: $____
Market Value: $____

4

Over The Rainbow
DC209 • 6"
Issued: 1994 • Ret./Susp.: 1997
Price Paid: $____
Market Value: $____

5

P. S. I Love You
DC203 • 2 ¼"
Issued: 1993 • Retired: 1997
Price Paid: $____
Market Value: $____

6 *New*

Panda Pal
10334 • 2-1/4"
Issued: 1998 • Current
Price Paid: $____
Market Value: $____

7 *New*

Peaceful Dreams
10331 • 4-3/4"
Issued: 1998 • Current
Price Paid: $____
Market Value: $____

8

Peacemaker (North Pole City Exclusive)
10257 • 3-3/4"
Issued: 1997 • Current
Price Paid: $____
Market Value: $____

9 *New*

Penguin Pal
10339 • 2-5/8"
Issued: 1998 • Current
Price Paid: $____
Market Value: $____

10

Piano Lesson
DC413 • 5 ½"
Issued: 1995 • Ret./Susp.: 1997
Price Paid: $____
Market Value: $____

CHERUBS

	Price Paid	Value of My Collection
1.		
2.		
3.		
4.		
5.		
6.		
7.		
8.		
9.		
10.		
PENCIL TOTALS		

CHERUBS

(1)

Piece Of My Heart
DC195 • 3"
Issued: 1995 • Current
Price Paid: $____
Market Value: $____

(2) New

Piggy Pal
10345 • 2 ¼"
Issued: 1998 • Current
Price Paid: $____
Market Value: $____

(3)

Pink Logo Sculpture
DC001 • 6 ½" wide
Issued: 1992 • Retired: 1994
Price Paid: $____
Market Value: $50

(4)

Pint-Sized Parade
DC323 • 3"
Issued: 1996 • Current
Price Paid: $____
Market Value: $____

(5) New

Playground Pony
10319 • 5 ⅜"
Issued: 1998 • Current
Price Paid: $____
Market Value: $____

(6) New

Please Be Mine
10259 • 3 ½"
Issued: 1998 • Current
Price Paid: $____
Market Value: $____

(7)

Poetry In Motion
(Special Edition)
DC113 • 5"
Issued: 1995 • Retired: 1997
Price Paid: $____
Market Value: $____

(8)

Pool Pals (July)
DC186 • 3 ¾"
Issued: 1994 • Retired: 1995
Price Paid: $____
Market Value: $55

(9)

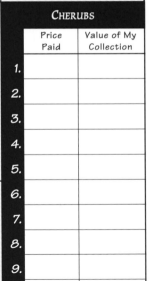

Pot Of Gold
(Early Release - Fall 1997)
10243 • 4 ⅛"
Issued: TBA • Current
Price Paid: $____
Market Value: $____

(10) New

Pray For Peace
10356 • 5"
Issued: 1998 • Current
Price Paid: $____
Market Value: $____

	Price Paid	Value of My Collection
1.		
2.		
3.		
4.		
5.		
6.		
7.		
8.		
9.		
10.		

CHERUBS

PENCIL TOTALS

Dreamsicles™ – VALUE GUIDE

①

Prayer Time
DC148 • 3"
Issued: 1996 • Current
Price Paid: $____
Market Value: $____

② New

Pretty Posies
(Early Release - Fall 1997)
10140 • 3 ⅛"
Issued: 1998 • Current
Price Paid: $____
Market Value: $____

③

Prima Ballerina
10051 • 4"
Issued: 1997 • Current
Price Paid: $____
Market Value: $____

④

Pumpkin Patch Cherub
DC206 • 3"
Issued: 1993 • Current
Price Paid: $____
Market Value: $____

⑤

Puppy And Me
DC052 • 3"
Issued: 1994 • Ret./Susp.: 1997
Price Paid: $____
Market Value: $____

⑥

Purr-fect Pals
DC239 • 4 ½"
Issued: 1995 • Ret./Susp.: 1997
Price Paid: $____
Market Value: $____

CHERUBS

	Price Paid	Value of My Collection
1.		
2.		
3.		
4.		
5.		
6.		
7.		
8.		
9.		
10.		
PENCIL TOTALS		

⑦

Ragamuffin
DC310 • 2 ¼"
Issued: 1995 • Current
Price Paid: $____
Market Value: $____

⑧

Rainbow Rider
DC236 • 4"
Issued: 1995 • Ret./Susp.: 1997
Price Paid: $____
Market Value: $____

⑨

Rainbow's End
DC311 • 2 ¼"
Issued: 1995 • Current
Price Paid: $____
Market Value: $____

⑩

Range Rider
DC305 • 4"
Issued: 1995 • Current
Price Paid: $____
Market Value: $____

1

Read Me A Story
DC123 • 2 ¾"
Issued: 1995 • Current
Price Paid: $____
Market Value: $____

2

Ready To Roll
DC424 • 4 ¼"
Issued: 1996 • Current
Price Paid: $____
Market Value: $____

3

Ride Like The Wind
(March)
DC182 • 4 ½"
Issued: 1994 • Retired: 1995
Price Paid: $____
Market Value: $55

4

Rock-A-Bye
DC158 • 2 ¾"
Issued: 1995 • Current
Price Paid: $____
Market Value: $____

5

Rock Away Rider
(Early Release - Fall 1997)
10123 • 3 ⅝"
Issued: TBA • Current
Price Paid: $____
Market Value: $____

6

Rose Garden
DC347 • 4 ¼"
Issued: 1996 • Suspended: 1996
Price Paid: $____
Market Value: $____

7

School Days (September)
DC188 • 4 ½"
Issued: 1994 • Retired: 1995
Price Paid: $____
Market Value: $55

8

Sealed With A Kiss
Issued: 1997 • Current
DC429 • 3 ½"
Price Paid: $____
Market Value: $____

9

Searching For Hope
(Fifth Avenue Exclusive)
DC019 • 4 ¾"
Issued: 1997 • Retired: 1997
Price Paid: $____
Market Value: $150

10

Seat Of Honor
DC426 • 4"
Issued: 1996 • Current
Price Paid: $____
Market Value: $____

	Price Paid	Value of My Collection
CHERUBS		
1.		
2.		
3.		
4.		
5.		
6.		
7.		
8.		
9.		
10.		
PENCIL TOTALS		

①

See No Evil
10041 • 5 ½"
Issued: 1997 • Current
Price Paid: $____
Market Value: $_____

②

Serenity
10176 • 1 ⅞"
Issued: 1997 • Current
Price Paid: $____
Market Value: $_____

③

Share The Fun
DC178 • 3 ½"
Issued: 1994 • Ret./Susp.: 1997
Price Paid: $____
Market Value: $_____

④

Shipmates
10001 • 6"
Issued: 1996 • Ret./Susp.: 1997
Price Paid: $____
Market Value: $_____

⑤

Side By Side
DC169 • 4 ¾"
Issued: 1994 • Retired: 1995
Price Paid: $____
Market Value: $_____

⑥

Sign Of Love
10158 • 3"
Issued: 1997 • Current
Price Paid: $____
Market Value: $_____

CHERUBS

	Price Paid	Value of My Collection
1.		
2.		
3.		
4.		
5.		
6.		
7.		
8.		
9.		
10.		
PENCIL TOTALS		

⑦

Signing Figurine
DC074 • 3 ½"
Issued: 1996 • Current
Price Paid: $____
Market Value: $_____

⑧ *New*

Sister I Love You
(Dreamsicles Expressions)
10274 • 3 ¾"
Issued: 1998 • Current
Price Paid: $____
Market Value: $_____

⑨

Sisters
DC427 • 3 ⅛"
Issued: 1997 • Current
Price Paid: $____
Market Value: $_____

⑩

Sitting Pretty
DC101 (5101) • 3 ¾"
Issued: 1991 • Retired: 1996
Price Paid: $____
Market Value: $14

(1)

Skater's Waltz
DC412 • 4 ½"
Issued: 1995 • Ret./Susp.: 1997
Price Paid: $____
Market Value: $____

(2)

Sleepover
DC421 • 4 ¾"
Issued: 1996 • Current
Price Paid: $____
Market Value: $____

(3)

Sleepy Head
DC086 • 2 ¾"
Issued: 1995 • Current
Price Paid: $____
Market Value: $____

(4)

Sleepyhead
(Early Release - Fall 1997)
10150 • 3 ⅞"
Issued: TBA • Current
Price Paid: $____
Market Value: $____

(5)

Sleigh Ride
DC122 • 5"
Issued: 1992 • Suspended: 1995
Price Paid: $____
Market Value: $____

(6)

Small Cherub With Hanging Ribbon
5104 • 4 ½"
Issued: 1991 • Suspended: 1992
Price Paid: $____
Market Value: $____

(7)

Snowflake
DC117 • 3 ¼"
Issued: 1994 • Suspended: 1996
Price Paid: $____
Market Value: $16

(8)

Snuggle Blanket
DC082 • 2 ⅜"
Issued: 1995 • Current
Price Paid: $____
Market Value: $____

(9)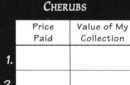

Snuggle Buddies
(GCC Exclusive)
DC017 • 5 ½"
Issued: 1996 • Retired: 1996
Price Paid: $____
Market Value: $30

(10)

Sock Hop
DC222 • 3 ¾"
Issued: 1994 • Suspended: 1995
Price Paid: $____
Market Value: $____

	CHERUBS	
	Price Paid	Value of My Collection
1.		
2.		
3.		
4.		
5.		
6.		
7.		
8.		
9.		
10.		
	PENCIL TOTALS	

1
New

Songbirds
(Early Release - Fall 1997)
10254 • 4"
Issued: 1998 • Current
Price Paid: $____
Market Value: $____

2

Speak No Evil
10042 • 5 ½"
Issued: 1997 • Current
Price Paid: $____
Market Value: $____

3

Special Delivery
(February)
DC181 • 5"
Issued: 1994 • Retired: 1995
Price Paid: $____
Market Value: $55

4

Special Occasions
Cherub (set/5)
10167 • 6 ¼"
Issued: 1997 • Current
Price Paid: $____
Market Value: $____

5

Springtime Frolic (April)
DC183 • 5"
Issued: 1994 • Retired: 1995
Price Paid: $____
Market Value: $55

6

Stairway To The Stars
DC348 • 5 ⅜"
Issued: 1996 • Suspended: 1996
Price Paid: $____
Market Value: $____

CHERUBS		
	Price Paid	Value of My Collection
1.		
2.		
3.		
4.		
5.		
6.		
7.		
8.		
9.		
10.		
PENCIL TOTALS		

7

Standing Ovation
10163 • 4 ¼"
Issued: 1997 • Current
Price Paid: $____
Market Value: $____

8

Star Bright
DC084 • 2 ¼"
Issued: 1995 • Current
Price Paid: $____
Market Value: $____

9

Star Gazers
DC308 • 4"
Issued: 1995 • Ret./Susp.: 1997
Price Paid: $____
Market Value: $____

10

A Star In One
DC318 • 3 ¼"
Issued: 1996 • Ret./Susp.: 1997
Price Paid: $____
Market Value: $____

1

Star Power
(Early Release - Fall 1997)
10128 • 3 ¾″
Issued: TBA • Suspended: 1997
Price Paid: $____
Market Value: $____

2 New

Stardust
10385 • 3 ¾″
Issued: 1998 • Current
Price Paid: $____
Market Value: $____

3

Starkeeping
DC360 • 3 ⅝″
Issued: 1996 • Suspended: 1996
Price Paid: $____
Market Value: $____

4

Starlight, Starbright
DC708 • 2″
Issued: 1995 • Ret./Susp.: 1997
Price Paid: $____
Market Value: $____

5

Star Makers
DC344 • 4 ½″
Issued: 1996 • Current
Price Paid: $____
Market Value: $____

6

Stolen Kiss
DC162 • 2 ¼″
Issued: 1994 • Current
Price Paid: $____
Market Value: $____

7

Straight From The Heart
DC314 • 5 ⅞″
Issued: 1996 • Ret./Susp.: 1997
Price Paid: $____
Market Value: $____

8

String Serenade
10168 • 6 ¾″
Issued: 1997 • Current
Price Paid: $____
Market Value: $____

9 New

A Stroll In The Park
10357 • 6 ¼″
Issued: 1998 • Current
Price Paid: $____
Market Value: $____

10

Sucking My Thumb
DC156 • 2″
Issued: 1994 • Retired: 1995
Price Paid: $____
Market Value: $15

	CHERUBS	
	Price Paid	Value of My Collection
1.		
2.		
3.		
4.		
5.		
6.		
7.		
8.		
9.		
10.		
	PENCIL TOTALS	

Dreamsicles™ — VALUE GUIDE

① Sugar 'N Spice
DC327 • 3 ⅛"
Issued: 1996 • Current
Price Paid: $____
Market Value: $____

② Sugarfoot
DC167 • 5"
Issued: 1994 • Ret./Susp.: 1997
Price Paid: $____
Market Value: $____

③ New
Sun Shower
(Early Release - Fall 1997)
10383 (10126) • 3 ½"
Issued: 1998 • Current
Price Paid: $____
Market Value: $____

④ Sunday Stroll
DC400 • 3 ⅞"
Issued: 1995 • Current
Price Paid: $____
Market Value: $____

⑤ Sunflower
DC221 • 2 ½"
Issued: 1996 • Current
Price Paid: $____
Market Value: $____

⑥ Super Star
DC704 • 6"
Issued: 1995 • Ret./Susp.: 1997
Price Paid: $____
Market Value: $____

CHERUBS	Price Paid	Value of My Collection
1.		
2.		
3.		
4.		
5.		
6.		
7.		
8.		
9.		
10.		
PENCIL TOTALS		

⑦ Surprise Gift
DC152 • 2"
Issued: 1994 • Retired: 1995
Price Paid: $____
Market Value: $15

⑧ Swan Lake
DC163 • 3 ½"
Issued: 1995 • Current
Price Paid: $____
Market Value: $____

⑨ Sweet Bouquet
DC081 • 2 ¼"
Issued: 1995 • Current
Price Paid: $____
Market Value: $____

⑩ Sweet Chariot
DC345 • 4"
Issued: 1996 • Current
Price Paid: $____
Market Value: $____

①

Sweet Charity
DC411 • 4 ¼"
Issued: 1995 • Ret./Susp.: 1997
Price Paid: $____
Market Value: $____

②

Sweet Dreams
DC125 • 11"
Issued: 1993 • Retired: 1995
Price Paid: $____
Market Value: $70

③

Sweet Gingerbread
DC223 • 3 ¾"
Issued: 1994 • Suspended: 1995
Price Paid: $____
Market Value: $____

④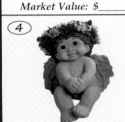

Sweet Pea
10038 • 3 ¾"
Issued: 1997 • Current
Price Paid: $____
Market Value: $____

⑤

Sweethearts
DC200 • 6"
Issued: 1994 • Ret./Susp.: 1997
Price Paid: $____
Market Value: $____

⑥

Sweetums
10161 • 3"
Issued: 1997 • Current
Price Paid: $____
Market Value: $____

⑦

Swimming For Hope
(Fifth Avenue Exclusive)
DC016 • 5"
Issued: 1996 • Retired: 1996
Price Paid: $____
Market Value: $____

⑧

Swing On A Star
DC208 • 5 ½"
Issued: 1994 • Ret./Susp.: 1997
Price Paid: $____
Market Value: $____

⑨

Swingtime
10044 • 4"
Issued: 1997 • Current
Price Paid: $____
Market Value: $____

⑩

Taking Aim
DC432 • 6" wide
Issued: 1997 • Current
Price Paid: $____
Market Value: $____

CHERUBS		
	Price Paid	Value of My Collection
1.		
2.		
3.		
4.		
5.		
6.		
7.		
8.		
9.		
10.		
	PENCIL TOTALS	

**① Tea Party
(GCC Exclusive)
DC015 • 3″**
Issued: 1996 • Retired: 1996
Price Paid: $____
Market Value: $52

**② Teacher's Pet
DC124 • 5″**
Issued: 1993 • Retired: 1997
Price Paid: $____
Market Value: $____

**③ Team Player
10164 • 3 ¾″**
Issued: 1997 • Current
Price Paid: $____
Market Value: $____

**④ Teddy And Me
DC053 • 3″**
Issued: 1994 • Ret./Susp.: 1997
Price Paid: $____
Market Value: $____

**⑤ Tender Loving Care
DC247 • 3 ¼″**
Issued: 1995 • Ret./Susp.: 1997
Price Paid: $____
Market Value: $____

**⑥ Thanks To You
DC316 • 3 ⅜″**
Issued: 1996 • Current
Price Paid: $____
Market Value: $____

CHERUBS

	Price Paid	Value of My Collection
1.		
2.		
3.		
4.		
5.		
6.		
7.		
8.		
9.		
10.		

PENCIL TOTALS

**⑦ Thanksgiving Cherubs
DC207 • 3 ¼″**
Issued: 1994 • Current
Price Paid: $____
Market Value: $____

**⑧ Thinking Of You
DC129 • 9″**
Issued: 1993 • Retired: 1997
Price Paid: $____
Market Value: $____

**⑨ Three Amigos
DC179 • 3 ¼″**
Issued: 1994 • Ret./Susp.: 1997
Price Paid: $____
Market Value: $____

**⑩ Three Wheelin'
DC401 • 4″**
Issued: 1995 • Current
Price Paid: $____
Market Value: $____

1

Tiger By The Tail
10182 • 4 ¼"
Issued: 1997 • Current
Price Paid: $____
Market Value: $____

2

Tiny Dancer
DC165 • 4 ½"
Issued: 1993 • Ret./Susp.: 1997
Price Paid: $____
Market Value: $____

3

Together Again
(Early Release - Fall 1997)
10246 • 4"
Issued: TBA • Suspended: 1997
Price Paid: $____
Market Value: $____

4

Topping The Tree
DC407 • 4"
Issued: 1995 • Current
Price Paid: $____
Market Value: $____

5

Twinkle Toes
DC091 • 2 ¼"
Issued: 1995 • Current
Price Paid: $____
Market Value: $____

6

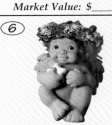

Twinkle, Twinkle
DC700 • 3 ½"
Issued: 1995 • Retired: 1997
Price Paid: $____
Market Value: $____

7

Twosome
DC149 • 5"
Issued: 1996 • Ret./Susp.: 1997
Price Paid: $____
Market Value: $____

8

Under The Big Top
DA251 • 5"
Issued: 1996 • Current
Price Paid: $____
Market Value: $____

9

New

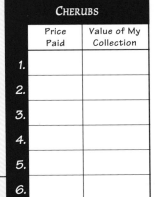

Unicorn Pal
10338 • 2 ½"
Issued: 1998 • Current
Price Paid: $____
Market Value: $____

10

Up All Night
DC155 • 2"
Issued: 1994 • Retired: 1995
Price Paid: $____
Market Value: $12

	CHERUBS	
	Price Paid	Value of My Collection
1.		
2.		
3.		
4.		
5.		
6.		
7.		
8.		
9.		
10.		
	PENCIL TOTALS	

① 	② 	③ New  AMERICAN CANCER SOCIETY.
Upsy Daisy! **DC085 • 2 ⅛″** Issued: 1995 • Current Price Paid: $____ *Market Value: $____*	**Vitality** **10172 • 2 ¼″** Issued: 1997 • Current Price Paid: $____ *Market Value: $____*	**We Are Winning (American Cancer Society Figurine)** **10380 • 3 ⅝″** Issued: 1998 • Current Price Paid: $____ *Market Value: $____*

④ 	⑤ 	⑥ 
We're Best Friends **DC715 • 6″** Issued: 1996 • Ret./Susp.: 1997 Price Paid: $____ *Market Value: $____*	**The Wedding March** **10121 • 6″** Issued: 1997 • Current Price Paid: $____ *Market Value: $____*	**Wedding Rehearsal** **DC134 • 5″** Issued: 1994 • Current Price Paid: $____ *Market Value: $____*

CHERUBS

	Price Paid	Value of My Collection
1.		
2.		
3.		
4.		
5.		
6.		
7.		
8.		
9.		
10.		
PENCIL TOTALS		

⑦ 	⑧ 
Wildflower **DC107 (5107) • 3 ½″** Issued: 1991 • Retired: 1996 Price Paid: $____ *Market Value: $12*	**Windy City (European Imports Exclusive)** **10151 • 5 ½″** Issued: 1997 • Current Price Paid: $____ *Market Value: $____*

⑨ 	⑩ 
A Wing And A Prayer **DC410 • 4 ¾″** Issued: 1995 • Current Price Paid: $____ *Market Value: $____*	**Winger** **DC319 • 3 ¼″** Issued: 1996 • Ret./Susp.: 1997 Price Paid: $____ *Market Value: $____*

1

Winter Ride
10177 • 5 ¾″
Issued: 1997 • Current
Price Paid: $____
Market Value: $____

2

**Winter Wonderland
(January)**
DC180 • 5 ½″
Issued: 1994 • Retired: 1995
Price Paid: $____
Market Value: $55

3

Wish You Were Here
10075 • 4 ⅛″
Issued: 1997 • Current
Price Paid: $____
Market Value: $____

4

Wishin' On A Star
DC120 • 4 ¼″
Issued: 1993 • Current
Price Paid: $____
Market Value: $____

5

Wishing 'N Hoping
DC328 • 3 ¼″
Issued: 1996 • Current
Price Paid: $____
Market Value: $____

6

Wishing Well
DC423 • 6 ¼″
Issued: 1996 • Current
Price Paid: $____
Market Value: $____

7

Wistful Thinking
DC707 • 2″
Issued: 1995 • Ret./Susp.: 1997
Price Paid: $____
Market Value: $____

8 New

**You're Special
(Dreamsicles Expressions)**
10275 • 3 ¾″
Issued: 1998 • Current
Price Paid: $____
Market Value: $____

9

You've Got A Friend
DC170 • 6″
Issued: 1994 • Ret./Susp.: 1997
Price Paid: $____
Market Value: $____

10

Young Love
DC214 • 2″
Issued: 1995 • Current
Price Paid: $____
Market Value: $____

CHERUBS

	Price Paid	Value of My Collection
1.		
2.		
3.		
4.		
5.		
6.		
7.		
8.		
9.		
10.		

PENCIL TOTALS

① Number Zero
DC071 • 3"
Issued: 1996 • Current
Price Paid: $____
Market Value: $_____

② First Birthday
DC061 • 2 ½"
Issued: 1995 • Current
Price Paid: $____
Market Value: $_____

③ Second Birthday
DC062 • 2 ½"
Issued: 1995 • Current
Price Paid: $____
Market Value: $_____

④ Third Birthday
DC063 • 2 ½"
Issued: 1995 • Current
Price Paid: $____
Market Value: $_____

⑤ Fourth Birthday
DC064 • 2 ¾"
Issued: 1995 • Current
Price Paid: $____
Market Value: $_____

⑥ Fifth Birthday
DC065 • 2 ¾"
Issued: 1995 • Current
Price Paid: $____
Market Value: $_____

CHERUBS
BIRTHDAY COLLECTION

	Price Paid	Value of My Collection
1.		
2.		
3.		
4.		
5.		
6.		
7.		
8.		
9.		
10.		
PENCIL TOTALS		

⑦ Sixth Birthday
DC066 • 2 ¾"
Issued: 1995 • Current
Price Paid: $____
Market Value: $_____

⑧ Seventh Birthday
DC067 • 3"
Issued: 1995 • Current
Price Paid: $____
Market Value: $_____

⑨ Eighth Birthday
DC068 • 3"
Issued: 1995 • Current
Price Paid: $____
Market Value: $_____

⑩ Ninth Birthday
DC069 • 3"
Issued: 1995 • Current
Price Paid: $____
Market Value: $_____

①

Alexandrite (June)
DC439 • 3 ½″
Issued: 1997 • Current
Price Paid: $____
Market Value: $____

②

Amethyst (February)
DC435 • 3 ½″
Issued: 1997 • Current
Price Paid: $____
Market Value: $____

③

Aquamarine (March)
DC436 • 3 ½″
Issued: 1997 • Current
Price Paid: $____
Market Value: $____

④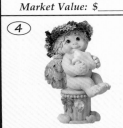

Diamond (April)
DC437 • 3 ¾″
Issued: 1997 • Current
Price Paid: $____
Market Value: $____

⑤

Emerald (May)
DC438 • 3 ¼″
Issued: 1997 • Current
Price Paid: $____
Market Value: $____

⑥

Garnet (January)
DC434 • 3 ⅝″
Issued: 1997 • Current
Price Paid: $____
Market Value: $____

⑦

Peridot (August)
DC441 • 3 ⅝″
Issued: 1997 • Current
Price Paid: $____
Market Value: $____

⑧

Rose Quartz (October)
DC443 • 3 ½″
Issued: 1997 • Current
Price Paid: $____
Market Value: $____

⑨

Ruby (July)
DC440 • 3 ¼″
Issued: 1997 • Current
Price Paid: $____
Market Value: $____

⑩

Sapphire (September)
DC442 • 3 ¾″
Issued: 1997 • Current
Price Paid: $____
Market Value: $____

CHERUBS
GEMSTONE COLLECTION

	Price Paid	Value of My Collection
1.		
2.		
3.		
4.		
5.		
6.		
7.		
8.		
9.		
10.		

PENCIL TOTALS

Dreamsicles™ — VALUE GUIDE

1

Topaz (November)
DC444 • 3 ¾"
Issued: 1997 • Current
Price Paid: $____
Market Value: $____

2

Turquoise (December)
DC445 • 3 ½"
Issued: 1997 • Current
Price Paid: $____
Market Value: $____

3

Baby And Me
DX054 • 3"
Issued: 1994 • Ret./Susp.: 1997
Price Paid: $____
Market Value: $____

4

Baby Love
DX147 • 2 ½"
Issued: 1992 • Retired: 1995
Price Paid: $____
Market Value: $____

5

Baby's First Christmas
DX242 • 3"
Issued: 1994 • Ret./Susp.: 1997
Price Paid: $____
Market Value: $____

6

Bearing Gifts
DX255 • 2 ½"
Issued: 1996 • Current
Price Paid: $____
Market Value: $____

CHERUBS
GEMSTONE COLLECTION

	Price Paid	Value of My Collection
1.		
2.		

HOLIDAY CHERUBS

3.		
4.		
5.		
6.		
7.		
8.		
9.		
10.		

PENCIL TOTALS

7

Bedtime Prayer
DX703 • 3"
Issued: 1995 • Ret./Susp.: 1997
Price Paid: $____
Market Value: $____

8

Best Buddies
DX159 • 3 ¾"
Issued: 1995 • Suspended: 1996
Price Paid: $____
Market Value: $____

9

Best Pals
DX103 • 4 ¾"
Issued: 1991 • Retired: 1994
Price Paid: $____
Market Value: $____

10

Birdie And Me
DX056 • 2 ½"
Issued: 1994 • Ret./Susp.: 1997
Price Paid: $____
Market Value: $____

1

Bluebird On My Shoulder
DX115 • 6″
Issued: 1992 • Retired: 1995
Price Paid: $____
Market Value: $____

2

Born This Day
DX230 • 4″
Issued: 1994 • Current
Price Paid: $____
Market Value: $____

3

Bright Eyes
DX108 • 3 ½″
Issued: 1991 • Suspended: 1996
Price Paid: $____
Market Value: $____

4

Bundle Of Joy
DX142 • 2 ½″
Issued: 1992 • Retired: 1995
Price Paid: $____
Market Value: $____

5

Bunny And Me
DX055 • 2 ⅝″
Issued: 1994 • Ret./Susp.: 1997
Price Paid: $____
Market Value: $____

6

Caroler #1
DX216 • 6 ½″
Issued: 1992 • Retired: 1995
Price Paid: $____
Market Value: $35

7

Caroler #2
DX217 • 6 ½″
Issued: 1992 • Retired: 1995
Price Paid: $____
Market Value: $35

8

Caroler #3
DX218 • 6 ½″
Issued: 1992 • Retired: 1995
Price Paid: $____
Market Value: $35

9

Cherub And Child
DX100 • 5 ½″
Issued: 1991 • Retired: 1995
Price Paid: $____
Market Value: $38

10

A Child's Prayer
DX145 • 2 ½″
Issued: 1992 • Retired: 1995
Price Paid: $____
Market Value: $____

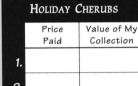

HOLIDAY CHERUBS

	Price Paid	Value of My Collection
1.		
2.		
3.		
4.		
5.		
6.		
7.		
8.		
.9.		
10.		

PENCIL TOTALS

HOLIDAY CHERUBS

Dreamsicles™ — VALUE GUIDE

①

Christmas Morning
DX710 • 3 ½"
Issued: 1995 • Ret./Susp.: 1997
Price Paid: $____
Market Value: $_____

②

Christmas Trim
DX711 • 2"
Issued: 1996 • Ret./Susp.: 1997
Price Paid: $____
Market Value: $_____

③

Come Let Us Adore Him
DX475 • 8 ¼"
Issued: 1995 • Ret./Susp.: 1997
Price Paid: $____
Market Value: $_____

④

Dream A Little Dream
DX144 • 2 ½"
Issued: 1992 • Retired: 1995
Price Paid: $____
Market Value: $_____

⑤

Follow Your Star
DX257 • 2 ½"
Issued: 1996 • Current
Price Paid: $____
Market Value: $_____

⑥

Forever Friends
DX102 • 4 ½"
Issued: 1991 • Retired: 1994
Price Paid: $____
Market Value: $_____

HOLIDAY CHERUBS

	Price Paid	Value of My Collection
1.		
2.		
3.		
4.		
5.		
6.		
7.		
8.		
9.		
10.		

PENCIL TOTALS

⑦

Forever Yours
DX110 • 10"
Issued: 1991 • Retired: 1995
Price Paid: $____
Market Value: $_____

⑧

Forty Winks
DX233 • 3 ½"
Issued: 1995 • Suspended: 1996
Price Paid: $____
Market Value: $_____

⑨

Free Bird
DX234 • 3 ¾"
Issued: 1995 • Suspended: 1996
Price Paid: $____
Market Value: $_____

⑩

Gingerbread House
DX254 • 2 ⅝"
Issued: 1996 • Current
Price Paid: $____
Market Value: $_____

① Good Shepherd
DX104 • 4"
Issued: 1994 • Ret./Susp.: 1997
Price Paid: $____
Market Value: $____

② Grandma's Or Bust
DX227 • 4"
Issued: 1995 • Suspended: 1996
Price Paid: $____
Market Value: $____

③ Granny's Cookies
DX228 • 2 ½"
Issued: 1995 • Suspended: 1996
Price Paid: $____
Market Value: $____

④ Happy Feet
DX164 • 3"
Issued: 1995 • Suspended: 1996
Price Paid: $____
Market Value: $____

⑤ Heavenly Dreamer
DX106 • 5 ½"
Issued: 1991 • Retired: 1996
Price Paid: $____
Market Value: $____

⑥ Hello Dolly
DX702 • 3 ½"
Issued: 1995 • Ret./Susp.: 1997
Price Paid: $____
Market Value: $____

⑦ Here Comes Trouble
DX214 • 8"
Issued: 1992 • Ret./Susp.: 1997
Price Paid: $____
Market Value: $____

⑧ Here's Looking At You
DX172 • 4"
Issued: 1994 • Retired: 1995
Price Paid: $____
Market Value: $____

⑨ Holiday Buddies
10185 • 3 ⅝"
Issued: 1997 • Current
Price Paid: $____
Market Value: $____

⑩ Holiday Pals
DX709 • 3 ¾"
Issued: 1995 • Ret./Susp.: 1997
Price Paid: $____
Market Value: $____

HOLIDAY CHERUBS

	Price Paid	Value of My Collection
1.		
2.		
3.		
4.		
5.		
6.		
7.		
8.		
9.		
10.		

PENCIL TOTALS

HOLIDAY CHERUBS

Dreamsicles™ — Value Guide

① Hugabye Baby
DX701 • 3″
Issued: 1995 • Retired: 1997
Price Paid: $____
Market Value: $_____

② Hushaby Baby
DX303 • 3 ¾″
Issued: 1995 • Suspended: 1996
Price Paid: $____
Market Value: $_____

③ I Love Mommy
DX226 • 2 ¾″
Issued: 1995 • Suspended: 1996
Price Paid: $____
Market Value: $_____

④ I Love You
DX225 • 4 ½″
Issued: 1995 • Suspended: 1996
Price Paid: $____
Market Value: $_____

⑤ Joyful Gathering
DX231 • 5″
Issued: 1994 • Current
Price Paid: $____
Market Value: $_____

⑥ Kitty And Me
DX051 • 3″
Issued: 1994 • Ret./Susp.: 1997
Price Paid: $____
Market Value: $_____

HOLIDAY CHERUBS

	Price Paid	Value of My Collection
1.		
2.		
3.		
4.		
5.		
6.		
7.		
8.		
9.		
10.		
PENCIL TOTALS		

⑦ Let's Play Fetch
DX237 • 4 ½″
Issued: 1995 • Suspended: 1996
Price Paid: $____
Market Value: $_____

⑧ Life Is Good
DX119 • 5 ¼″
Issued: 1992 • Retired: 1996
Price Paid: $____
Market Value: $_____

⑨ Little Darlin'
DX146 • 2 ½″
Issued: 1992 • Retired: 1995
Price Paid: $____
Market Value: $_____

⑩ Littlest Angel
DX143 • 2 ½″
Issued: 1992 • Retired: 1995
Price Paid: $____
Market Value: $_____

(1)

Love My Kitty
DX130 • 3 ¾"
Issued: 1993 • Retired: 1996
Price Paid: $____
Market Value: $_____

(2)

Love My Puppy
DX131 • 3 ¾"
Issued: 1993 • Retired: 1996
Price Paid: $____
Market Value: $_____

(3)

Love My Teddy
DX132 • 4"
Issued: 1993 • Retired: 1996
Price Paid: $____
Market Value: $_____

(4)

Make A Wish
DX118 • 5 ½"
Issued: 1992 • Suspended: 1996
Price Paid: $____
Market Value: $_____

(5)

Mall Santa
DX258 • 6"
Issued: 1996 • Current
Price Paid: $____
Market Value: $_____

(6)

Me And My Shadow
DX116 • 5 ½"
Issued: 1993 • Retired: 1996
Price Paid: $____
Market Value: $_____

(7)

Mischief Maker
DX105 • 5"
Issued: 1991 • Retired: 1996
Price Paid: $____
Market Value: $_____

(8)

Miss Morningstar
DX141 • 7 ¼"
Issued: 1993 • Retired: 1996
Price Paid: $____
Market Value: $_____

(9)

Moon Dance
DX210 • 5 ½"
Issued: 1995 • Retired: 1996
Price Paid: $____
Market Value: $_____

(10)

Moonglow
DX235 • 3 ¾"
Issued: 1995 • Suspended: 1996
Price Paid: $____
Market Value: $_____

HOLIDAY CHERUBS

	Price Paid	Value of My Collection
1.		
2.		
3.		
4.		
5.		
6.		
7.		
8.		
9.		
10.		
	PENCIL TOTALS	

Dreamsicles™ — VALUE GUIDE

1

My Prayer
DX121 • 5 ½"
Issued: 1992 • Suspended: 1996
Price Paid: $____
Market Value: $____

2

Newborn Cherub
DX168 • 3" wide
Issued: 1994 • Suspended: 1996
Price Paid: $____
Market Value: $____

3

'Nite 'Nite
DX238 • 4 ½"
Issued: 1995 • Suspended: 1996
Price Paid: $____
Market Value: $____

4

Noel
DX712 • 2 ⅜"
Issued: 1996 • Ret./Susp.: 1997
Price Paid: $____
Market Value: $____

5

Nursery Rhyme
DX229 • 7"
Issued: 1995 • Suspended: 1995
Price Paid: $____
Market Value: $____

6

Oh Little Star
DX713 • 2 ¼"
Issued: 1996 • Ret./Susp.: 1997
Price Paid: $____
Market Value: $____

HOLIDAY CHERUBS

	Price Paid	Value of My Collection
1.		
2.		
3.		
4.		
5.		
6.		
7.		
8.		
9.		
10.		

PENCIL TOTALS

7

Open Me First
DX243 • 3 ¼"
Issued: 1994 • Ret./Susp.: 1997
Price Paid: $____
Market Value: $____

8

Over The Rainbow
DX209 • 6"
Issued: 1995 • Suspended: 1996
Price Paid: $____
Market Value: $____

9

Poetry In Motion
(Special Edition)
DX113 • 5"
Issued: 1995 • Retired: 1997
Price Paid: $____
Market Value: $98

10

Puppy And Me
DX052 • 3"
Issued: 1994 • Ret./Susp.: 1997
Price Paid: $____
Market Value: $____

①

Purr-fect Pals
DX239 • 4 ½"
Issued: 1995 • Suspended: 1996
Price Paid: $____
Market Value: $_____

②

Rainbow Rider
DX236 • 4"
Issued: 1995 • Suspended: 1996
Price Paid: $____
Market Value: $_____

③

Range Rider
DX305 • 4"
Issued: 1995 • Suspended: 1996
Price Paid: $____
Market Value: $_____

④

Read Me A Story
DX123 • 2 ¾"
Issued: 1995 • Suspended: 1996
Price Paid: $____
Market Value: $_____

⑤

Santa Baby
DX256 • 2 ¼"
Issued: 1996 • Current
Price Paid: $____
Market Value: $_____

⑥

Santa's Little Helper
DX109 • 4"
Issued: 1991 • Ret./Susp.: 1997
Price Paid: $____
Market Value: $_____

⑦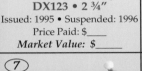

Santa's Shop
10186 • 4 ½"
Issued: 1997 • Current
Price Paid: $____
Market Value: $_____

⑧

Share The Fun
DX178 • 3 ½"
Issued: 1994 • Suspended: 1996
Price Paid: $____
Market Value: $_____

⑨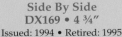

Side By Side
DX169 • 4 ¾"
Issued: 1994 • Retired: 1995
Price Paid: $____
Market Value: $_____

⑩

Sitting Pretty
DX101 • 3 ¾"
Issued: 1991 • Retired: 1996
Price Paid: $____
Market Value: $_____

HOLIDAY CHERUBS

	Price Paid	Value of My Collection
1.		
2.		
3.		
4.		
5.		
6.		
7.		
8.		
9.		
10.		

PENCIL TOTALS

HOLIDAY CHERUBS

(1)
Sleigh Ride
DX122 • 5"
Issued: 1992 • Ret./Susp.: 1997
Price Paid: $____
Market Value: $____

(2)
Small Cherub With Hanging Ribbon
5104C • 4 ½"
Issued: 1991 • Suspended: 1992
Price Paid: $____
Market Value: $50

(3)
Snowbound
(Early Release - Fall 1997)
10120 • 4 ½"
Issued: TBA • Current
Price Paid: $____
Market Value: $____

(4)
Snowflake
DX117 • 3 ¼"
Issued: 1994 • Current
Price Paid: $____
Market Value: $____

(5)
Starlight, Starbright
DX708 • 2"
Issued: 1995 • Ret./Susp.: 1997
Price Paid: $____
Market Value: $____

(6)
Stolen Kiss
DX162 • 2 ¼"
Issued: 1994 • Suspended: 1996
Price Paid: $____
Market Value: $____

Holiday Cherubs

	Price Paid	Value of My Collection
1.		
2.		
3.		
4.		
5.		
6.		
7.		
8.		
9.		
10.		
PENCIL TOTALS		

(7)
Super Star
DX704 • 6"
Issued: 1995 • Ret./Susp.: 1997
Price Paid: $____
Market Value: $____

(8)
Swan Lake
DX163 • 3 ½"
Issued: 1995 • Suspended: 1996
Price Paid: $____
Market Value: $____

(9)
Sweet Dreams
DX125 • 11"
Issued: 1993 • Retired: 1995
Price Paid: $____
Market Value: $____

(10)
Swing On A Star
DX208 • 5 ½"
Issued: 1995 • Suspended: 1996
Price Paid: $____
Market Value: $____

HOLIDAY CHERUBS

1

Teacher's Pet
DX124 • 5"
Issued: 1993 • Retired: 1997
Price Paid: $____
Market Value: $____

2

Teddy And Me
DX053 • 3"
Issued: 1994 • Ret./Susp.: 1997
Price Paid: $____
Market Value: $____

3

Thinking of You
DX129 • 9"
Issued: 1993 • Retired: 1997
Price Paid: $____
Market Value: $____

4

Three Amigos
DX179 • 3 ¼"
Issued: 1994 • Suspended: 1996
Price Paid: $____
Market Value: $____

5

Toyland
(Early Release - Fall 1997)
10255 • 4"
Issued: TBA • Current
Price Paid: $____
Market Value: $____

6

Twinkle, Twinkle
DX700 • 3 ½"
Issued: 1995 • Retired: 1997
Price Paid: $____
Market Value: $____

7

Two Log Night
(Early Release - Fall 1997)
10119 • 4"
Issued: TBA • Current
Price Paid: $____
Market Value: $____

8

Under The Mistletoe
DX253 • 4 ⅛"
Issued: 1996 • Current
Price Paid: $____
Market Value: $____

9

Visions Of Sugarplums
DX300 • 5 ½"
Issued: 1996 • Current
Price Paid: $____
Market Value: $____

10

Wildflower
DX107 • 3 ½"
Issued: 1991 • Retired: 1996
Price Paid: $____
Market Value: $____

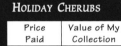

HOLIDAY CHERUBS

	Price Paid	Value of My Collection
1.		
2.		
3.		
4.		
5.		
6.		
7.		
8.		
9.		
10.		
PENCIL TOTALS		

Dreamsicles™ — Value Guide

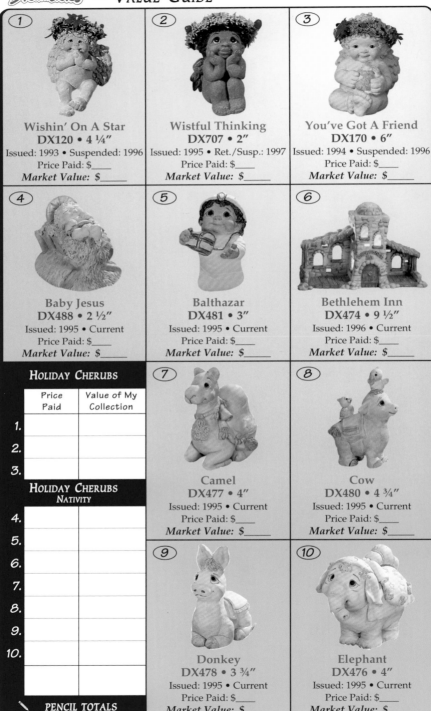

① Wishin' On A Star
DX120 • 4 ¼"
Issued: 1993 • Suspended: 1996
Price Paid: $____
Market Value: $_____

② Wistful Thinking
DX707 • 2"
Issued: 1995 • Ret./Susp.: 1997
Price Paid: $____
Market Value: $_____

③ You've Got A Friend
DX170 • 6"
Issued: 1994 • Suspended: 1996
Price Paid: $____
Market Value: $_____

④ Baby Jesus
DX488 • 2 ½"
Issued: 1995 • Current
Price Paid: $____
Market Value: $_____

⑤ Balthazar
DX481 • 3"
Issued: 1995 • Current
Price Paid: $____
Market Value: $_____

⑥ Bethlehem Inn
DX474 • 9 ½"
Issued: 1996 • Current
Price Paid: $____
Market Value: $_____

HOLIDAY CHERUBS

	Price Paid	Value of My Collection
1.		
2.		
3.		

HOLIDAY CHERUBS
NATIVITY

4.		
5.		
6.		
7.		
8.		
9.		
10.		

PENCIL TOTALS

⑦ Camel
DX477 • 4"
Issued: 1995 • Current
Price Paid: $____
Market Value: $_____

⑧ Cow
DX480 • 4 ¾"
Issued: 1995 • Current
Price Paid: $____
Market Value: $_____

⑨ Donkey
DX478 • 3 ¾"
Issued: 1995 • Current
Price Paid: $____
Market Value: $_____

⑩ Elephant
DX476 • 4"
Issued: 1995 • Current
Price Paid: $____
Market Value: $_____

1

Gaspar
DX483 • 3 ⅛"
Issued: 1995 • Current
Price Paid: $____
Market Value: $____

2

Horse
DX479 • 4"
Issued: 1995 • Current
Price Paid: $____
Market Value: $____

3

Joseph
DX485 • 3 ½"
Issued: 1995 • Current
Price Paid: $____
Market Value: $____

4

Mary
DX484 • 2 ⅞"
Issued: 1995 • Current
Price Paid: $____
Market Value: $____

5

Melchior
DX482 • 3 ½"
Issued: 1995 • Current
Price Paid: $____
Market Value: $____

6

Shepherd And Sheep
DX486 • 3 ¾"
Issued: 1995 • Current
Price Paid: $____
Market Value: $____

7

Three Lambs (set/3)
DX487 • 2"
Issued: 1995 • Current
Price Paid: $____
Market Value: $____

8

Nativity Collection (set/15)
DX489 • various
Issued: 1995 • Current
Price Paid: $____
Market Value: $____

HOLIDAY CHERUBS

	Price Paid	Value of My Collection
1.		
2.		
3.		
4.		
5.		
6.		
7.		
8.		

HOLIDAY CHERUBS
NATIVITY

PENCIL TOTALS

HOLIDAY CHERUBS

Dreamsicles™ — VALUE GUIDE

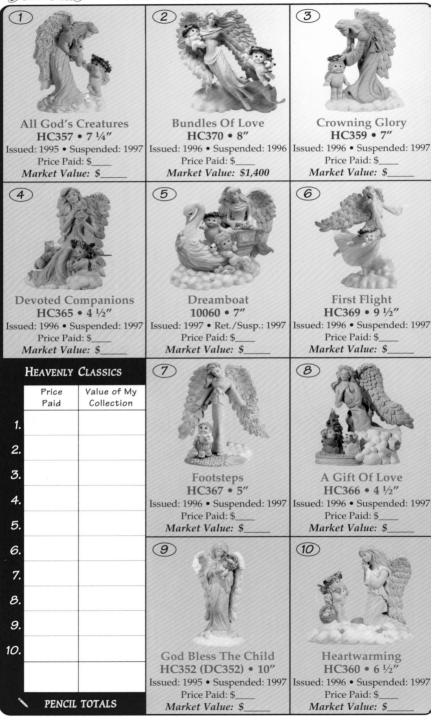

① All God's Creatures
HC357 • 7 ¼"
Issued: 1995 • Suspended: 1997
Price Paid: $____
Market Value: $_____

② Bundles Of Love
HC370 • 8"
Issued: 1996 • Suspended: 1996
Price Paid: $____
Market Value: $1,400

③ Crowning Glory
HC359 • 7"
Issued: 1996 • Suspended: 1997
Price Paid: $____
Market Value: $_____

④ Devoted Companions
HC365 • 4 ½"
Issued: 1996 • Suspended: 1997
Price Paid: $____
Market Value: $_____

⑤ Dreamboat
10060 • 7"
Issued: 1997 • Ret./Susp.: 1997
Price Paid: $____
Market Value: $_____

⑥ First Flight
HC369 • 9 ½"
Issued: 1996 • Suspended: 1997
Price Paid: $____
Market Value: $_____

⑦ Footsteps
HC367 • 5"
Issued: 1996 • Suspended: 1997
Price Paid: $____
Market Value: $_____

⑧ A Gift Of Love
HC366 • 4 ½"
Issued: 1996 • Suspended: 1997
Price Paid: $____
Market Value: $_____

⑨ God Bless The Child
HC352 (DC352) • 10"
Issued: 1995 • Suspended: 1997
Price Paid: $____
Market Value: $_____

⑩ Heartwarming
HC360 • 6 ½"
Issued: 1996 • Suspended: 1997
Price Paid: $____
Market Value: $_____

HEAVENLY CLASSICS

	Price Paid	Value of My Collection
1.		
2.		
3.		
4.		
5.		
6.		
7.		
8.		
9.		
10.		

PENCIL TOTALS

Higher Learning
HC353 (DC353) • 6 ½"
Issued: 1995 • Suspended: 1997
Price Paid: $____
Market Value: $____

Hush Little Baby
HC361 • 7 ¼"
Issued: 1996 • Suspended: 1997
Price Paid: $____
Market Value: $____

Making Memories
HC381 • 11"
Issued: 1996 • Suspended: 1996
Price Paid: $____
Market Value: $____

Making Memories
10096 • 11"
Issued: 1997 • Suspended: 1997
Price Paid: $____
Market Value: $____

Music Appreciation
HC354 (DC354) • 5 ½"
Issued: 1995 • Suspended: 1997
Price Paid: $____
Market Value: $____

Nature's Blessing
HC364 • 3 ¾"
Issued: 1996 • Suspended: 1997
Price Paid: $____
Market Value: $____

New Beginnings
10251 • 6 ¼"
Issued: 1997 • Current
Price Paid: $____
Market Value: $____

Ode To Joy
HC362 • 6 ¾"
Issued: 1996 • Suspended: 1997
Price Paid: $____
Market Value: $____

On Wings Of Love
HC355 (DC355) • 9 ½"
Issued: 1995 • Suspended: 1997
Price Paid: $____
Market Value: $____

Our Father
HC356 • 4 ¾"
Issued: 1995 • Suspended: 1997
Price Paid: $____
Market Value: $____

HEAVENLY CLASSICS

	Price Paid	Value of My Collection
1.		
2.		
3.		
4.		
5.		
6.		
7.		
8.		
9.		
10.		

PENCIL TOTALS

HEAVENLY CLASSICS

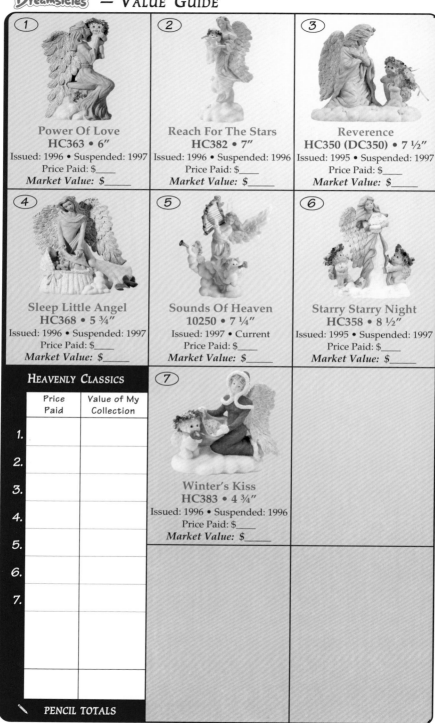

Dreamsicles™ — VALUE GUIDE

① Power Of Love
HC363 • 6"
Issued: 1996 • Suspended: 1997
Price Paid: $____
Market Value: $____

② Reach For The Stars
HC382 • 7"
Issued: 1996 • Suspended: 1996
Price Paid: $____
Market Value: $____

③ Reverence
HC350 (DC350) • 7 ½"
Issued: 1995 • Suspended: 1997
Price Paid: $____
Market Value: $____

④ Sleep Little Angel
HC368 • 5 ¾"
Issued: 1996 • Suspended: 1997
Price Paid: $____
Market Value: $____

⑤ Sounds Of Heaven
10250 • 7 ¼"
Issued: 1997 • Current
Price Paid: $____
Market Value: $____

⑥ Starry Starry Night
HC358 • 8 ½"
Issued: 1995 • Suspended: 1997
Price Paid: $____
Market Value: $____

⑦ Winter's Kiss
HC383 • 4 ¾"
Issued: 1996 • Suspended: 1996
Price Paid: $____
Market Value: $____

HEAVENLY CLASSICS

	Price Paid	Value of My Collection
1.		
2.		
3.		
4.		
5.		
6.		
7.		
✎ PENCIL TOTALS		

(1)

All I Want
DK040 • 3 ⅜"
Issued: 1996 • Ret./Susp.: 1997
Price Paid: $____
Market Value: $____

(2)
**Anticipation
(I.C.E. Figurine)**
SP002 • 4 ¼"
Issued: 1997 • Current
Price Paid: $____
Market Value: $____

(3)

Apple Dumpling
10059 • 3 ⅞"
Issued: 1997 • Current
Price Paid: $____
Market Value: $____

(4)

Apple Polisher
10058 • 4 ⅛"
Issued: 1997 • Current
Price Paid: $____
Market Value: $____

(5)

Arctic Pals
10178 • 2 ¾"
Issued: 1997 • Current
Price Paid: $____
Market Value: $____

(6)

Baby Bunny
10065 • 4"
Issued: 1997 • Current
Price Paid: $____
Market Value: $____

(7)

Bear Back Rider
DK025 • 4 ½"
Issued: 1996 • Ret./Susp.: 1997
Price Paid: $____
Market Value: $____

(8)

Beggars' Night
10204 • 4 ¼"
Issued: 1997 • Current
Price Paid: $____
Market Value: $____

(9)

By The Sea
10055 • 3 ½"
Issued: 1997 • Current
Price Paid: $____
Market Value: $____

(10)

Child's Play
DK018 • 2 ⅞"
Issued: 1996 • Current
Price Paid: $____
Market Value: $____

DREAMSICLES KIDS

	Price Paid	Value of My Collection
1.		
2.		
3.		
4.		
5.		
6.		
7.		
8.		
9.		
10.		
PENCIL TOTALS		

DREAMSICLES KIDS

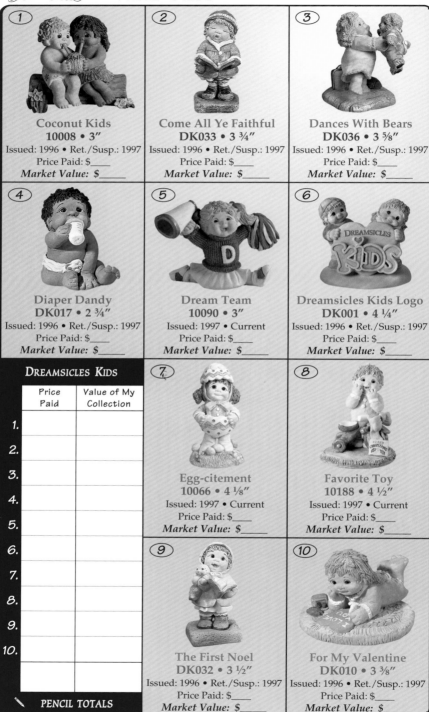

1

Coconut Kids
10008 • 3"
Issued: 1996 • Ret./Susp.: 1997
Price Paid: $____
Market Value: $____

2

Come All Ye Faithful
DK033 • 3 ¾"
Issued: 1996 • Ret./Susp.: 1997
Price Paid: $____
Market Value: $____

3

Dances With Bears
DK036 • 3 ⅝"
Issued: 1996 • Ret./Susp.: 1997
Price Paid: $____
Market Value: $____

4

Diaper Dandy
DK017 • 2 ¾"
Issued: 1996 • Ret./Susp.: 1997
Price Paid: $____
Market Value: $____

5

Dream Team
10090 • 3"
Issued: 1997 • Current
Price Paid: $____
Market Value: $____

6

Dreamsicles Kids Logo
DK001 • 4 ¼"
Issued: 1996 • Ret./Susp.: 1997
Price Paid: $____
Market Value: $____

DREAMSICLES KIDS

	Price Paid	Value of My Collection
1.		
2.		
3.		
4.		
5.		
6.		
7.		
8.		
9.		
10.		

PENCIL TOTALS

7

Egg-citement
10066 • 4 ⅛"
Issued: 1997 • Current
Price Paid: $____
Market Value: $____

8

Favorite Toy
10188 • 4 ½"
Issued: 1997 • Current
Price Paid: $____
Market Value: $____

9

The First Noel
DK032 • 3 ½"
Issued: 1996 • Ret./Susp.: 1997
Price Paid: $____
Market Value: $____

10

For My Valentine
DK010 • 3 ⅜"
Issued: 1996 • Ret./Susp.: 1997
Price Paid: $____
Market Value: $____

DREAMSICLES KIDS

1

Free Kittens
DK038 • 2 ⅞"
Issued: 1996 • Current
Price Paid: $____
Market Value: $____

2

Free Puppies
DK039 • 2 ¾"
Issued: 1996 • Current
Price Paid: $____
Market Value: $____

3

Frosty Friends
10179 • 2 ½"
Issued: 1997 • Current
Price Paid: $____
Market Value: $____

4

Here's My List
DK022 • 3 ½"
Issued: 1996 • Ret./Susp.: 1997
Price Paid: $____
Market Value: $____

5

High Chair High Jinks
DK030 • 3 ⅜"
Issued: 1996 • Ret./Susp.: 1997
Price Paid: $____
Market Value: $____

6

Honey Bunny
DK016 • 2 ¼"
Issued: 1996 • Current
Price Paid: $____
Market Value: $____

7

Hug A Bunny
DK015 • 4"
Issued: 1996 • Ret./Susp.: 1997
Price Paid: $____
Market Value: $____

8

Hula Honeys
10011 • 3 ½"
Issued: 1996 • Ret./Susp.: 1997
Price Paid: $____
Market Value: $____

9

Joy To The World
DK031 • 4"
Issued: 1996 • Ret./Susp.: 1997
Price Paid: $____
Market Value: $____

10

Junior Nurse
DK029 • 3"
Issued: 1996 • Current
Price Paid: $____
Market Value: $____

DREAMSICLES KIDS

	Price Paid	Value of My Collection
1.		
2.		
3.		
4.		
5.		
6.		
7.		
8.		
9.		
10.		

PENCIL TOTALS

DREAMSICLES KIDS

①

Kissing Booth
DK042 • 3 ⅜″
Issued: 1997 • Current
Price Paid: $____
Market Value: $_____

②

Light The Candles
DK026 • 2 ¾″
Issued: 1996 • Ret./Susp.: 1997
Price Paid: $____
Market Value: $_____

③

Lion's Share
DA663 • 4 ¼″
Issued: 1996 • Current
Price Paid: $____
Market Value: $_____

④

Love You, Mom
DK011 • 3 ¾″
Issued: 1996 • Current
Price Paid: $____
Market Value: $_____

⑤

Mama's Girl
DK019 • 2 ¾″
Issued: 1996 • Ret./Susp.: 1997
Price Paid: $____
Market Value: $_____

⑥

Mush You Huskies
10180 • 12″
Issued: 1997 • Current
Price Paid: $____
Market Value: $_____

DREAMSICLES KIDS

	Price Paid	Value of My Collection
1.		
2.		
3.		
4.		
5.		
6.		
7.		
8.		
9.		
10.		
PENCIL TOTALS		

⑦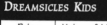

My A-B-C's
DK012 • 3″
Issued: 1996 • Ret./Susp.: 1997
Price Paid: $____
Market Value: $_____

⑧

Nutcracker Sweet
10189 • 3 ¼″
Issued: 1997 • Current
Price Paid: $____
Market Value: $_____

⑨

Ocean Friends
10010 • 5 ½″
Issued: 1996 • Ret./Susp.: 1997
Price Paid: $____
Market Value: $_____

⑩

Piggy Bank
DK024 • 3″
Issued: 1996 • Ret./Susp.: 1997
Price Paid: $____
Market Value: $_____

1

Please, Santa
DK023 • 3 ½"
Issued: 1996 • Ret./Susp.: 1997
Price Paid: $____
Market Value: $_____

2

Pop Goes The Weasel
DK014 • 2 ½"
Issued: 1996 • Ret./Susp.: 1997
Price Paid: $____
Market Value: $_____

3

Potty Break
10056 • 3"
Issued: 1997 • Current
Price Paid: $____
Market Value: $_____

4

Potty Time
10057 • 3"
Issued: 1997 • Current
Price Paid: $____
Market Value: $_____

5

Pull Toy
DK027 • 4 ¼"
Issued: 1996 • Current
Price Paid: $____
Market Value: $_____

6

Punkin
10203 • 4 ½"
Issued: 1997 • Current
Price Paid: $____
Market Value: $_____

7

Rhyme Time
DK013 • 2 ¾"
Issued: 1996 • Ret./Susp.: 1997
Price Paid: $____
Market Value: $_____

8

Sand, Sun And Fun
10054 • 2 ⅞"
Issued: 1997 • Current
Price Paid: $____
Market Value: $_____

9

Silent Night
DK034 • 3 ⅜"
Issued: 1996 • Ret./Susp.: 1997
Price Paid: $____
Market Value: $_____

10

Snowball Fight
DK037 • 3 ⅝"
Issued: 1996 • Ret./Susp.: 1997
Price Paid: $____
Market Value: $_____

DREAMSICLES KIDS

	Price Paid	Value of My Collection
1.		
2.		
3.		
4.		
5.		
6.		
7.		
8.		
9.		
10.		
PENCIL TOTALS		

DREAMSICLES KIDS

1
Spilt Milk
10053 • 4 ¼"
Issued: 1997 • Ret./Susp.: 1997
Price Paid: $____
Market Value: $_____

2
Sunken Treasure
10009 • 3 ½"
Issued: 1996 • Ret./Susp.: 1997
Price Paid: $____
Market Value: $_____

3
Surf's Up
10007 • 3 ½"
Issued: 1996 • Ret./Susp.: 1997
Price Paid: $____
Market Value: $_____

4
Three Bears
DK035 • 2 ½"
Issued: 1996 • Ret./Susp.: 1997
Price Paid: $____
Market Value: $_____

5
Three Musketeers
DA664 • 4"
Issued: 1996 • Current
Price Paid: $____
Market Value: $_____

6
Toddlin' Tyke
DK020 • 3"
Issued: 1996 • Current
Price Paid: $____
Market Value: $_____

DREAMSICLES KIDS

	Price Paid	Value of My Collection
1.		
2.		
3.		
4.		
5.		
6.		
7.		
8.		

BEARS

9.		
10.		

PENCIL TOTALS

7
Visit With Santa
DK021 • 3 ¾"
Issued: 1996 • Ret./Susp.: 1997
Price Paid: $____
Market Value: $_____

8
Young Pups
DK028 • 3 ¼"
Issued: 1996 • Ret./Susp.: 1997
Price Paid: $____
Market Value: $_____

9
Beary Sweet
DA455 • 5"
Issued: 1994 • Suspended: 1996
Price Paid: $____
Market Value: $25

10
Buddy Bear
DA451 (5051) • 2 ½"
Issued: 1991 • Retired: 1994
Price Paid: $____
Market Value: $12

1

Clara Bear
DA454 • 5 ½″
Issued: 1995 • Suspended: 1996
Price Paid: $____
Market Value: $____

2

Country Bear
DA458 • 5″
Issued: 1993 • Suspended: 1996
Price Paid: $____
Market Value: $20

3

Mama Bear
DA452 (5052) • 3 ½″
Issued: 1991 • Retired: 1994
Price Paid: $____
Market Value: $12

4

Pierre The Bear
DA453 • 4″
Issued: 1993 • Suspended: 1996
Price Paid: $____
Market Value: $20

5

Pierre The Bear
DX453 • 4″
Issued: 1993 • Suspended: 1996
Price Paid: $____
Market Value: $____

6

Teddy Bear
DA456 (5056) • 4 ½″
Issued: 1992 • Suspended: 1995
Price Paid: $____
Market Value: $20

7

Wedding Bears
DA457 (5057) • 5 ¼″
Issued: 1992 • Suspended: 1996
Price Paid: $____
Market Value: $____

8

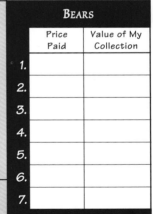

Dodo
DA482 (5082) • 3 ½″
Issued: 1992 • Retired: 1994
Price Paid: $____
Market Value: $____

9

Lazy Bones
DA605 • 3″
Issued: 1992 • Suspended: 1993
Price Paid: $____
Market Value: $____

10

Papa Pelican
DA602 • 8 ½″
Issued: 1992 • Retired: 1994
Price Paid: $____
Market Value: $38

BEARS		
	Price Paid	Value of My Collection
1.		
2.		
3.		
4.		
5.		
6.		
7.		
BIRDS		
8.		
9.		
10.		
PENCIL TOTALS		

BEARS/BIRDS

91

Dreamsicles™ — VALUE GUIDE

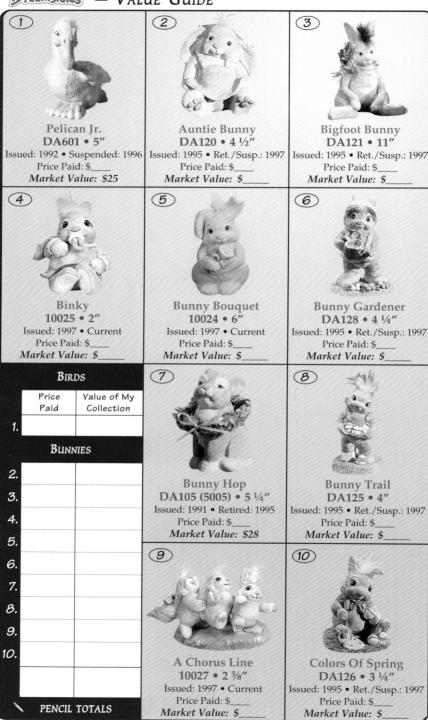

① Pelican Jr.
DA601 • 5″
Issued: 1992 • Suspended: 1996
Price Paid: $____
Market Value: $25

② Auntie Bunny
DA120 • 4 ½″
Issued: 1995 • Ret./Susp.: 1997
Price Paid: $____
Market Value: $____

③ Bigfoot Bunny
DA121 • 11″
Issued: 1995 • Ret./Susp.: 1997
Price Paid: $____
Market Value: $____

④ Binky
10025 • 2″
Issued: 1997 • Current
Price Paid: $____
Market Value: $____

⑤ Bunny Bouquet
10024 • 6″
Issued: 1997 • Current
Price Paid: $____
Market Value: $____

⑥ Bunny Gardener
DA128 • 4 ¼″
Issued: 1995 • Ret./Susp.: 1997
Price Paid: $____
Market Value: $____

	Price Paid	Value of My Collection
BIRDS		
1.		
BUNNIES		
2.		
3.		
4.		
5.		
6.		
7.		
8.		
9.		
10.		
PENCIL TOTALS		

⑦ Bunny Hop
DA105 (5005) • 5 ¼″
Issued: 1991 • Retired: 1995
Price Paid: $____
Market Value: $28

⑧ Bunny Trail
DA125 • 4″
Issued: 1995 • Ret./Susp.: 1997
Price Paid: $____
Market Value: $____

⑨ A Chorus Line
10027 • 2 ⅝″
Issued: 1997 • Current
Price Paid: $____
Market Value: $____

⑩ Colors Of Spring
DA126 • 3 ¼″
Issued: 1995 • Ret./Susp.: 1997
Price Paid: $____
Market Value: $____

①

Cupid's Helper
DA203 • 2 ¼"
Issued: 1995 • Current
Price Paid: $____
Market Value: $____

②

Dimples
DA100 (5000) • 2 ¼"
Issued: 1991 • Retired: 1995
Price Paid: $____
Market Value: $12

③

Easter Surprise
DA115 • 4 ¼"
Issued: 1993 • Ret./Susp.: 1997
Price Paid: $____
Market Value: $____

④

Egg-citing
DA131 • 2"
Issued: 1995 • Current
Price Paid: $____
Market Value: $____

⑤

Gathering Flowers
DA320 (5320) • 4 ½"
Issued: 1991 • Retired: 1995
Price Paid: $____
Market Value: $30

⑥

Gathering Flowers
DX320 • 4 ½"
Issued: 1991 • Retired: 1993
Price Paid: $____
Market Value: $____

⑦

Helga
DA112 (5012) • 3 ¼"
Issued: 1992 • Retired: 1995
Price Paid: $____
Market Value: $____

⑧

Hippity Hop
DA106 (5006) • 9"
Issued: 1991 • Retired: 1994
Price Paid: $____
Market Value: $40

⑨

Hitchin' A Ride
DA321 (5321) • 4 ½"
Issued: 1991 • Ret./Susp.: 1997
Price Paid: $____
Market Value: $____

⑩

Honey Bun
DA101 (5001) • 2 ¼"
Issued: 1991 • Retired: 1995
Price Paid: $____
Market Value: $12

BUNNIES

	Price Paid	Value of My Collection
1.		
2.		
3.		
4.		
5.		
6.		
7.		
8.		
9.		
10.		
PENCIL TOTALS		

BUNNIES

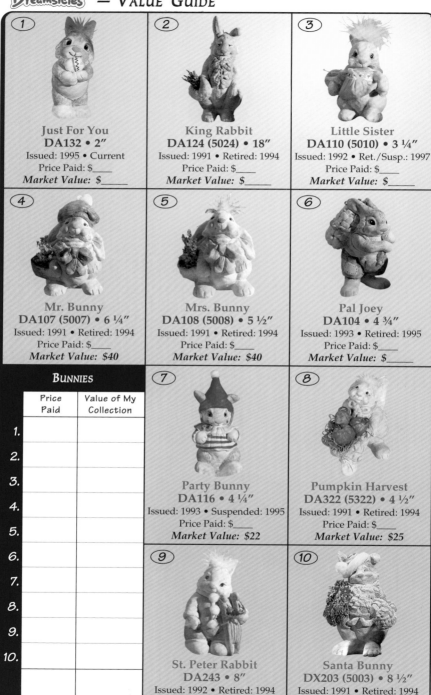

1
Just For You
DA132 • 2"
Issued: 1995 • Current
Price Paid: $____
Market Value: $____

2
King Rabbit
DA124 (5024) • 18"
Issued: 1991 • Retired: 1994
Price Paid: $____
Market Value: $____

3
Little Sister
DA110 (5010) • 3 ¼"
Issued: 1992 • Ret./Susp.: 1997
Price Paid: $____
Market Value: $____

4
Mr. Bunny
DA107 (5007) • 6 ¼"
Issued: 1991 • Retired: 1994
Price Paid: $____
Market Value: $40

5
Mrs. Bunny
DA108 (5008) • 5 ½"
Issued: 1991 • Retired: 1994
Price Paid: $____
Market Value: $40

6
Pal Joey
DA104 • 4 ¾"
Issued: 1993 • Retired: 1995
Price Paid: $____
Market Value: $____

BUNNIES

	Price Paid	Value of My Collection
1.		
2.		
3.		
4.		
5.		
6.		
7.		
8.		
9.		
10.		

PENCIL TOTALS

7
Party Bunny
DA116 • 4 ¼"
Issued: 1993 • Suspended: 1995
Price Paid: $____
Market Value: $22

8
Pumpkin Harvest
DA322 (5322) • 4 ½"
Issued: 1991 • Retired: 1994
Price Paid: $____
Market Value: $25

9
St. Peter Rabbit
DA243 • 8"
Issued: 1992 • Retired: 1994
Price Paid: $____
Market Value: $____

10
Santa Bunny
DX203 (5003) • 8 ½"
Issued: 1991 • Retired: 1994
Price Paid: $____
Market Value: $40

1

Sarge
DA111 (5011) • 3 ¼″
Issued: 1992 • Retired: 1995
Price Paid: $____
Market Value: $12

2

Scooter Bunny
DA129 • 2 ½″
Issued: 1995 • Ret./Susp.: 1997
Price Paid: $____
Market Value: $____

3

Sir Hareold
DA123 (5023) • 10 ½″
Issued: 1992 • Retired: 1996
Price Paid: $____
Market Value: $60

4

Soap Box Bunny
DA221 (5303) • 4″
Issued: 1991 • Retired: 1995
Price Paid: $____
Market Value: $25

5

Sonny Boy
DA109 (5009) • 3 ¼″
Issued: 1992 • Ret./Susp.: 1997
Price Paid: $____
Market Value: $____

6

Steppin' Out
DA130 • 2 ½″
Issued: 1995 • Current
Price Paid: $____
Market Value: $____

7

Sweetie Pie
10026 • 2 ¼″
Issued: 1997 • Current
Price Paid: $____
Market Value: $____

8

Tiny Bunny
DA102 (5002) • 3″
Issued: 1991 • Retired: 1995
Price Paid: $____
Market Value: $14

9

A Tisket, A Tasket
DA114 • 4 ½″
Issued: 1993 • Ret./Susp.: 1997
Price Paid: $____
Market Value: $____

10

Tuckered Out
DA127 • 4 ¾″
Issued: 1995 • Current
Price Paid: $____
Market Value: $____

BUNNIES

	Price Paid	Value of My Collection
1.		
2.		
3.		
4.		
5.		
6.		
7.		
8.		
9.		
10.		
	PENCIL TOTALS	

BUNNIES

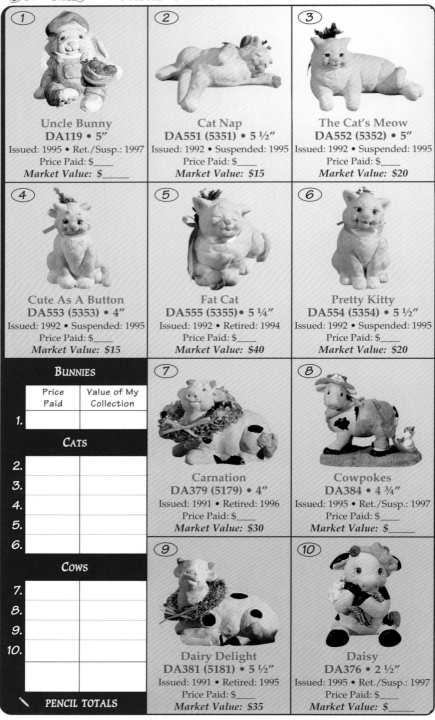

① **Uncle Bunny**
DA119 • 5"
Issued: 1995 • Ret./Susp.: 1997
Price Paid: $____
Market Value: $_____

② **Cat Nap**
DA551 (5351) • 5 ½"
Issued: 1992 • Suspended: 1995
Price Paid: $____
Market Value: $15

③ **The Cat's Meow**
DA552 (5352) • 5"
Issued: 1992 • Suspended: 1995
Price Paid: $____
Market Value: $20

④ **Cute As A Button**
DA553 (5353) • 4"
Issued: 1992 • Suspended: 1995
Price Paid: $____
Market Value: $15

⑤ **Fat Cat**
DA555 (5355) • 5 ¼"
Issued: 1992 • Retired: 1994
Price Paid: $____
Market Value: $40

⑥ **Pretty Kitty**
DA554 (5354) • 5 ½"
Issued: 1992 • Suspended: 1995
Price Paid: $____
Market Value: $20

BUNNIES

	Price Paid	Value of My Collection
1.		

CATS

2.		
3.		
4.		
5.		
6.		

COWS

7.		
8.		
9.		
10.		

PENCIL TOTALS

⑦ **Carnation**
DA379 (5179) • 4"
Issued: 1991 • Retired: 1996
Price Paid: $____
Market Value: $30

⑧ **Cowpokes**
DA384 • 4 ¾"
Issued: 1995 • Ret./Susp.: 1997
Price Paid: $____
Market Value: $_____

⑨ **Dairy Delight**
DA381 (5181) • 5 ½"
Issued: 1991 • Retired: 1995
Price Paid: $____
Market Value: $35

⑩ **Daisy**
DA376 • 2 ½"
Issued: 1995 • Ret./Susp.: 1997
Price Paid: $____
Market Value: $_____

① Get Along Little Dogie
DA378 (5178) • 3 ½"
Issued: 1991 • Ret./Susp.: 1997
Price Paid: $____
Market Value: $_____

② Henrietta
DA383 • 7" wide
Issued: 1994 • Retired: 1996
Price Paid: $____
Market Value: $35

③ Hey Diddle Diddle
DA380 (5180) • 5 ¼"
Issued: 1991 • Retired: 1996
Price Paid: $___
Market Value: $25

④ Moo Cow
DA377 • 4"
Issued: 1993 • Ret./Susp.: 1997
Price Paid: $____
Market Value: $_____

⑤ Santa Cow
DX455 • 4 ¾"
Issued: 1995 • Ret./Susp.: 1997
Price Paid: $____
Market Value: $_____

⑥ Sweet Cream
DA382 (5182) • 7 ¼"
Issued: 1991 • Retired: 1996
Price Paid: $____
Market Value: $45

⑦ Hound Dog
DA568 • 3"
Issued: 1992 • Retired: 1994
Price Paid: $____
Market Value: $25

⑧ Man's Best Friend
DA560 • 3 ½"
Issued: 1992 • Retired: 1994
Price Paid: $____
Market Value: $18

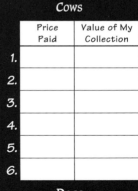

⑨ Puppy Love
DA562 • 3 ½"
Issued: 1992 • Retired: 1994
Price Paid: $____
Market Value: $18

⑩ Red Rover
DA566 • 5 ½"
Issued: 1992 • Retired: 1994
Price Paid: $____
Market Value: $25

Cows	Price Paid	Value of My Collection
1.		
2.		
3.		
4.		
5.		
6.		

Dogs		
7.		
8.		
9.		
10.		

PENCIL TOTALS

Cows/Dogs

1

Scooter
DA567 • 3"
Issued: 1992 • Retired: 1994
Price Paid: $____
Market Value: $18

2

Baby Jumbo
10028 • 3 ⅛"
Issued: 1997 • Current
Price Paid: $____
Market Value: $____

3

Center Ring
DA250 • 3"
Issued: 1996 • Current
Price Paid: $____
Market Value: $____

4

Elephant Walk
DA253 • 5 ½"
Issued: 1996 • Current
Price Paid: $____
Market Value: $____

5

Intermission
DA254 • 2 ¼"
Issued: 1996 • Current
Price Paid: $____
Market Value: $____

6

Peanut Gallery
DA256 • 3 ¼"
Issued: 1996 • Current
Price Paid: $____
Market Value: $____

7

Showtime
DA255 • 5"
Issued: 1996 • Current
Price Paid: $____
Market Value: $____

8

Trunkful Of Love
10029 • 3 ¼"
Issued: 1997 • Current
Price Paid: $____
Market Value: $____

9

Blowfish
DA608 • 1"
Issued: 1992 • Suspended: 1993
Price Paid: $____
Market Value: $20

10

Double Fish
DA611 • 2 ½"
Issued: 1992 • Suspended: 1993
Price Paid: $____
Market Value: $____

	Price Paid	Value of My Collection
DOGS		
1.		
ELEPHANTS		
2.		
3.		
4.		
5.		
6.		
7.		
8.		
FISH		
9.		
10.		
PENCIL TOTALS		

Largemouth Bass
DA609 • 3"
Issued: 1992 • Suspended: 1993
Price Paid: $____
Market Value: $____

Needlenose Fish
DA610 • 3 ½"
Issued: 1992 • Suspended: 1993
Price Paid: $____
Market Value: $20

Boo Babies (set/4)
DA655 • 2"
Issued: 1994 • Current
Price Paid: $____
Market Value: $____

Boo Who?
DA650 • 4 ½"
Issued: 1991 • Retired: 1996
Price Paid: $____
Market Value: $15

Goblins Galore
DA656 • 7 ¼" wide
Issued: 1995 • Current
Price Paid: $____
Market Value: $____

Trick Or Treat
DA651 • 4 ½"
Issued: 1991 • Retired: 1996
Price Paid: $____
Market Value: $15

Lambie Pie
DA328 (5028) • 4"
Issued: 1991 • Retired: 1994
Price Paid: $____
Market Value: $20

Mutton Chops
DA326 (5026) • 2 ½"
Issued: 1991 • Retired: 1994
Price Paid: $____
Market Value: $15

Socrates The Sheep
5029 • 5"
Issued: 1991 • Suspended: 1992
Price Paid: $____
Market Value: $____

Wooley Bully
DA327 (5027) • 2 ¾"
Issued: 1991 • Retired: 1994
Price Paid: $____
Market Value: $20

FISH	Price Paid	Value of My Collection
1.		
2.		
GHOSTS & GOBLINS		
3.		
4.		
5.		
6.		
LAMBS & SHEEP		
7.		
8.		
9.		
10.		
PENCIL TOTALS		

FISH/GHOSTS/LAMBS

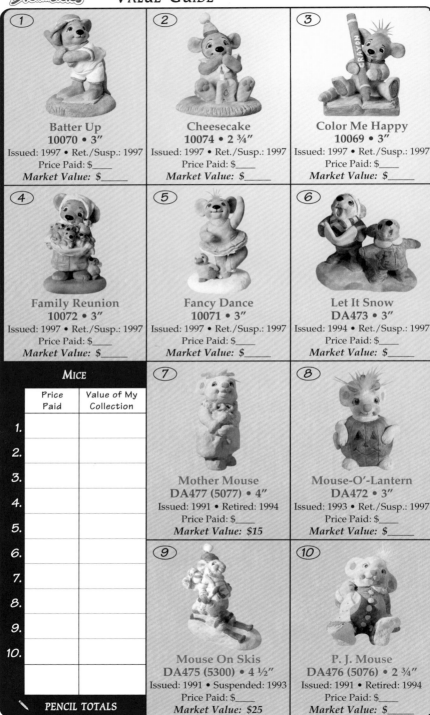

1

Batter Up
10070 • 3"
Issued: 1997 • Ret./Susp.: 1997
Price Paid: $____
Market Value: $_____

2

Cheesecake
10074 • 2 ¾"
Issued: 1997 • Ret./Susp.: 1997
Price Paid: $____
Market Value: $_____

3

Color Me Happy
10069 • 3"
Issued: 1997 • Ret./Susp.: 1997
Price Paid: $____
Market Value: $_____

4

Family Reunion
10072 • 3"
Issued: 1997 • Ret./Susp.: 1997
Price Paid: $____
Market Value: $_____

5

Fancy Dance
10071 • 3"
Issued: 1997 • Ret./Susp.: 1997
Price Paid: $____
Market Value: $_____

6

Let It Snow
DA473 • 3"
Issued: 1994 • Ret./Susp.: 1997
Price Paid: $____
Market Value: $_____

MICE

	Price Paid	Value of My Collection
1.		
2.		
3.		
4.		
5.		
6.		
7.		
8.		
9.		
10.		

PENCIL TOTALS

7

Mother Mouse
DA477 (5077) • 4"
Issued: 1991 • Retired: 1994
Price Paid: $____
Market Value: $15

8

Mouse-O'-Lantern
DA472 • 3"
Issued: 1993 • Ret./Susp.: 1997
Price Paid: $____
Market Value: $_____

9

Mouse On Skis
DA475 (5300) • 4 ½"
Issued: 1991 • Suspended: 1993
Price Paid: $____
Market Value: $25

10

P. J. Mouse
DA476 (5076) • 2 ¾"
Issued: 1991 • Retired: 1994
Price Paid: $____
Market Value: $_____

① Sleigh Bells Ring
DA474 • 2 ¾"
Issued: 1994 • Ret./Susp.: 1997
Price Paid: $____
Market Value: $____

② Sweet On You
10073 • 2 ½"
Issued: 1997 • Ret./Susp.: 1997
Price Paid: $____
Market Value: $____

③ Little Drummer Boy
DX241 • 6"
Issued: 1992 • Suspended: 1996
Price Paid: $____
Market Value: $____

④ Musician With Cymbals
5154 • 7 ¼"
Issued: 1991 • Suspended: 1992
Price Paid: $____
Market Value: $85

⑤ Musician With Drums
5152 • 8"
Issued: 1991 • Suspended: 1992
Price Paid: $____
Market Value: $95

⑥ Musician With Flute
5153 • 7 ½"
Issued: 1991 • Suspended: 1992
Price Paid: $____
Market Value: $85

⑦ Musician With Trumpet
5151 • 7"
Issued: 1991 • Suspended: 1992
Price Paid: $____
Market Value: $95

⑧ Hambone
DA344 (5044) • 3 ¼"
Issued: 1991 • Retired: 1996
Price Paid: $____
Market Value: $18

⑨ Hamlet
DA342 (5042) • 4 ¼"
Issued: 1991 • Retired: 1996
Price Paid: $____
Market Value: $18

⑩ Kitchen Pig
DA345 (5045) • 8 ½"
Issued: 1991 • Suspended: 1995
Price Paid: $____
Market Value: $50

MICE

	Price Paid	Value of My Collection
1.		
2.		

MUSICIANS

3.		
4.		
5.		
6.		
7.		

PIGS

8.		
9.		
10.		

PENCIL TOTALS

MICE/MUSICIANS/PIGS

1 Momma Pig
DA347 • 4 ½"
Issued: 1994 • Suspended: 1996
Price Paid: $____
Market Value: $30

2 Pappy Pig
DA346 • 4 ¾"
Issued: 1994 • Suspended: 1996
Price Paid: $____
Market Value: $____

3 Piglet
DA343 (5043) • 3"
Issued: 1991 • Retired: 1996
Price Paid: $____
Market Value: $18

4 Pigmalion
DA340 (5040) • 2"
Issued: 1991 • Retired: 1995
Price Paid: $____
Market Value: $12

5 Pigtails
DA341 (5041) • 2"
Issued: 1991 • Retired: 1995
Price Paid: $____
Market Value: $12

6 Pintsize Pigs
DA349 • 3 ½"
Issued: 1994 • Suspended: 1996
Price Paid: $____
Market Value: $35

7 Preppie Pig
DA348 • 4 ½"
Issued: 1994 • Suspended: 1996
Price Paid: $____
Market Value: $28

8 Elf Help
DX259 • 3 ¼"
Issued: 1996 • Ret./Susp.: 1997
Price Paid: $____
Market Value: $____

9 Father Christmas
DX246 • 8 ½"
Issued: 1993 • Ret./Susp.: 1997
Price Paid: $____
Market Value: $____

10 Here Comes Santa Claus
DX245 • 18"
Issued: 1991 • Ret./Susp.: 1997
Price Paid: $____
Market Value: $____

PIGS

	Price Paid	Value of My Collection
1.		
2.		
3.		
4.		
5.		
6.		
7.		

SANTAS & ELVES

8.		
9.		
10.		

PENCIL TOTALS

①

Jolly Old Santa
DX244 • 7 ½"
Issued: 1992 • Ret./Susp.: 1997
Price Paid: $____
Market Value: $____

②

Santa's Elf
DX240 • 5 ½"
Issued: 1991 • Retired: 1996
Price Paid: $____
Market Value: $____

③

Be-Witching
DA652 • 5"
Issued: 1993 • Current
Price Paid: $____
Market Value: $____

④

Halloween Ride
DA659 • 4"
Issued: 1994 • Current
Price Paid: $____
Market Value: $____

⑤

Pumpkin Seed
DA662 • 3"
Issued: 1994 • Current
Price Paid: $____
Market Value: $____

⑥

Sweeping Beauty
DA661 • 2 ½"
Issued: 1994 • Current
Price Paid: $____
Market Value: $____

⑦

Witch
DA660 • 5"
Issued: 1991 • Current
Price Paid: $____
Market Value: $____

⑧

Witch's Brew
DA654 • 4"
Issued: 1994 • Current
Price Paid: $____
Market Value: $____

⑨

Armadillo
5176 • 3 ½"
Issued: 1991 • Suspended: 1992
Price Paid: $____
Market Value: $____

⑩

Beach Baby
DA615 • 6 ½"
Issued: 1992 • Retired: 1994
Price Paid: $____
Market Value: $____

SANTAS & ELVES

	Price Paid	Value of My Collection
1.		
2.		

WITCHES

3.		
4.		
5.		
6.		
7.		
8.		

OTHER FIGURINES

9.		
10.		

PENCIL TOTALS

SANTAS/WITCHES/OTHER

①

Crabby
DA607 • 2 ½"
Issued: 1992 • Suspended: 1993
Price Paid: $____
Market Value: $32

②

Dino
DA480 (5080) • 4 ¼"
Issued: 1992 • Retired: 1994
Price Paid: $____
Market Value: $____

③

Free Ride
DA631 (5031) • 3 ½"
Issued: 1992 • Suspended: 1996
Price Paid: $____
Market Value: $28

④

Happy Sailing
DA220 (5301) • 3 ¾"
Issued: 1991 • Retired: 1994
Price Paid: $____
Market Value: $____

⑤

Li'l Chick
DA385 • 2"
Issued: 1993 • Suspended: 1995
Price Paid: $____
Market Value: $14

⑥

Li'l Duck
DA388 • 2"
Issued: 1993 • Suspended: 1995
Price Paid: $____
Market Value: $14

OTHER FIGURINES

	Price Paid	Value of My Collection
1.		
2.		
3.		
4.		
5.		
6.		
7.		
8.		
9.		
10.		

PENCIL TOTALS

⑦

Naptime
DA556 • 2 ¾"
Issued: 1996 • Suspended: 1996
Price Paid: $____
Market Value: $20

⑧

Octopus' Garden
DA606 • 4"
Issued: 1992 • Suspended: 1993
Price Paid: $____
Market Value: $30

⑨

Opening Night
DA252 • 4"
Issued: 1996 • Current
Price Paid: $____
Market Value: $____

⑩

Prancer
DX202 • 8"
Issued: 1991 • Ret./Susp.: 1997
Price Paid: $____
Market Value: $____

①

Rhino
DA481 (5081) • 4″
Issued: 1992 • Retired: 1994
Price Paid: $____
Market Value: $_____

②

Ricky Raccoon
5170 • 6 ½″
Issued: 1991 • Suspended: 1992
Price Paid: $____
Market Value: $_____

③

Scarecrow & Friends
DA653 • 3″
Issued: 1993 • Current
Price Paid: $____
Market Value: $_____

④

Slow Poke
DA630 (5030) • 4 ½″
Issued: 1992 • Suspended: 1995
Price Paid: $____
Market Value: $20

⑤

Snowman
DX252 • 3 ½″
Issued: 1991 • Suspended: 1996
Price Paid: $____
Market Value: $_____

⑥

Splash
DA616 • 6 ¼″
Issued: 1993 • Retired: 1994
Price Paid: $____
Market Value: $_____

⑦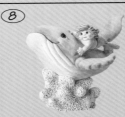

Three On A Sled
DX454 • 4″
Issued: 1994 • Ret./Susp.: 1997
Price Paid: $____
Market Value: $_____

⑧

Water Ballet
10006 • 5″
Issued: 1996 • Ret./Susp.: 1997
Price Paid: $____
Market Value: $_____

⑨

Winter's Comin'
DA471 (5171) • 4 ½″
Issued: 1991 • Suspended: 1993
Price Paid: $____
Market Value: $25

OTHER FIGURINES

	Price Paid	Value of My Collection
1.		
2.		
3.		
4.		
5.		
6.		
7.		
8.		
9.		

PENCIL TOTALS

OTHER FIGURINES

1 New

Birthday Surprise
(Early Release - Fall 1997)
♪*My Favorite Things*
10152 • 5 ⅛"
Issued: 1998 • Current
Price Paid: $_____
Market Value: $_____

2

Carousel Ride
♪*Carousel Waltz*
DS283 • 11 ¼"
Issued: 1996 • Current
Price Paid: $_____
Market Value: $_____

3 New

Cherub Twirler
♪*Music Box Dancer*
10363 • 5 ¾"
Issued: 1998 • Current
Price Paid: $_____
Market Value: $_____

4

Coming To Town
♪*Santa Claus Is Coming*
To Town
10206 • 6"
Issued: 1997 • Current
Price Paid: $_____
Market Value: $_____

5

Dance Ballerina Dance
♪*Music Box Dancer*
DC140 • 8"
Issued: 1992 • Retired: 1995
Price Paid: $_____
Market Value: $75

6 New

Flying High
♪*Wind Beneath My Wings*
10302 • 7 ¼"
Issued: 1998 • Current
Price Paid: $_____
Market Value: $_____

MUSICALS & WATERGLOBES
CHERUBS

	Price Paid	Value of My Collection
1.		
2.		
3.		
4.		
5.		
6.		
7.		
8.		
9.		
10.		

PENCIL TOTALS

7

The Flying Lesson
♪*We've Only Just Begun*
DS281 • 5"
Issued: 1996 • Ret./Susp.: 1997
Price Paid: $_____
Market Value: $_____

8

Jumbo Ride
♪*You Light Up My Life*
10049 • 6 ½"
Issued: 1997 • Ret./Susp.: 1997
Price Paid: $_____
Market Value: $_____

9

Merry-Go-Round
♪*Memories*
DS278 • 7"
Issued: 1995 • Ret./Susp.: 1997
Price Paid: $_____
Market Value: $_____

10

Moonstruck
♪*You've Got A Friend*
DS277 • 7"
Issued: 1995 • Ret./Susp.: 1997
Price Paid: $_____
Market Value: $_____

① Oh Christmas Tree
♪*O Tannenbaum*
DS276 • 7 ⅛"
Issued: 1995 • Ret./Susp.: 1997
Price Paid: $____
Market Value: $____

② Pirouette
♪*Music Box Dancer*
DS279 • 6 ½"
Issued: 1995 • Ret./Susp.: 1997
Price Paid: $____
Market Value: $____

③ Shooting Star
♪*Twinkle, Twinkle Little Star*
DS275 • 6 ⅛"
Issued: 1995 • Ret./Susp.: 1997
Price Paid: $____
Market Value: $____

④ New
Sleep Tight
(Early Release - Fall 1997)
♪*Rock A Bye Baby*
10153 • 4 ¼"
Issued: 1998 • Current
Price Paid: $____
Market Value: $____

⑤ Star Of Wonder
♪*Silent Night*
10149 • 5 ½"
Issued: 1997 • Current
Price Paid: $____
Market Value: $____

⑥ Stolen Kiss
♪*Love Story*
DS282 • 5 ¾"
Issued: 1996 • Ret./Susp.: 1997
Price Paid: $____
Market Value: $____

⑦ Swanderful
♪*Memories*
10048 • 6 ½"
Issued: 1997 • Ret./Susp.: 1997
Price Paid: $____
Market Value: $____

⑧ Teeter Tots
♪*Over The Rainbow*
DS280 • 6"
Issued: 1996 • Ret./Susp.: 1997
Price Paid: $____
Market Value: $____

⑨ New
Together Forever
♪*Endless Love*
10303 • 7"
Issued: 1998 • Current
Price Paid: $____
Market Value: $____

⑩ Wedding Vows
♪*The Wedding March*
10223 • 6"
Issued: 1997 • Current
Price Paid: $____
Market Value: $____

MUSICALS & WATERGLOBES
CHERUBS

	Price Paid	Value of My Collection
1.		
2.		
3.		
4.		
5.		
6.		
7.		
8.		
9.		
10.		
	PENCIL TOTALS	

MUSICALS & WATERGLOBES

①

Whale Of A Time
♪You've Got A Friend
10047 • 6 ¼"
Issued: 1997 • Ret./Susp.: 1997
Price Paid: $____
Market Value: $_____

②

Dance With Me
♪Dance of The Sugarplum Fairy
HC103 • 6"
Issued: 1996 • Ret./Susp.: 1997
Price Paid: $____
Market Value: $_____

③

Dreamboat
(Early Release - Fall 1997)
♪Wind Beneath My Wings
10154 • 6 ¼"
Issued: TBA • Current
Price Paid: $____
Market Value: $_____

④

God Bless The Child
HC107 • 5"
Issued: 1996 • Ret./Susp.: 1997
Price Paid: $____
Market Value: $_____

⑤

Heart To Heart
♪Cherish
HC100 • 6"
Issued: 1996 • Ret./Susp.: 1997
Price Paid: $____
Market Value: $_____

⑥

Hush Little Baby
HC104 • 4 ½"
Issued: 1996 • Ret./Susp.: 1997
Price Paid: $____
Market Value: $_____

Musicals & Waterglobes
Cherubs

	Price Paid	Value of My Collection
1.		

Musicals & Waterglobes
Heavenly Classics

2.		
3.		
4.		
5.		
6.		
7.		
8.		
9.		
10.		

PENCIL TOTALS

⑦

Music Lesson
♪Memories
HC102 • 6"
Issued: 1996 • Ret./Susp.: 1997
Price Paid: $____
Market Value: $_____

⑧

My Special Angel
♪Impossible Dream
HC101 • 5 ½"
Issued: 1996 • Ret./Susp.: 1997
Price Paid: $____
Market Value: $_____

⑨

On Wings Of Love
HC106 • 5"
Issued: 1996 • Ret./Susp.: 1997
Price Paid: $____
Market Value: $_____

⑩

Our Father
HC105 • 4 ½"
Issued: 1996 • Ret./Susp.: 1997
Price Paid: $____
Market Value: $_____

1

Star Seekers (revolving)
♪ *Somewhere Out There*
HC109 • 6"
Issued: 1996 • Ret./Susp.: 1997
Price Paid: $____
Market Value: $____

2

Starry Starry Night
HC108 • 5"
Issued: 1996 • Ret./Susp.: 1997
Price Paid: $____
Market Value: $____

3

The Finishing Touches
DS201 • 4 ½"
Issued: 1995 • Retired: 1995
Price Paid: $____
Market Value: $20

4

Santa In Dreamsicle Land
DS216 • 4 ½"
Issued: 1996 • Retired: 1996
Price Paid: $____
Market Value: $20

5

Star Of Wonder
10143 • 4"
Issued: 1997 • Retired: 1997
Price Paid: $____
Market Value: $____

6

Bunny Bookends (pair)
DA122 (5022) • 5 ¼"
Issued: 1992 • Suspended: 1995
Price Paid: $____
Market Value: $____

7

Bunny Bookends (pair)
5021 • 5 ¼"
Issued: 1992 • Suspended: 1992
Price Paid: $____
Market Value: $____

8
New

Cherub Bookends (pair)
10403 • 6 ½"
Issued: 1998 • Current
Price Paid: $____
Market Value: $____

9
New

Cherub Bookends (pair)
10404 • 6 ½"
Issued: 1998 • Current
Price Paid: $____
Market Value: $____

10

Little Dickens
DC127 • 5 ½"
Issued: 1993 • Retired: 1995
Price Paid: $____
Market Value: $35

MUSICALS & WATERGLOBES
HEAVENLY CLASSICS

	Price Paid	Value of My Collection
1.		
2.		

BELLS

3.		
4.		
5.		

BOOKENDS

6.		
7.		
8.		
9.		
10.		

PENCIL TOTALS

MUSICALS/BELLS/BOOKENDS

1

Little Dickens
DX127 • 5 ½"
Issued: 1993 • Retired: 1995
Price Paid: $_____
Market Value: $_____

2

Long Fellow
DC126 • 5 ½"
Issued: 1993 • Retired: 1995
Price Paid: $_____
Market Value: $38

3

Long Fellow
DX126 • 5 ½"
Issued: 1993 • Retired: 1995
Price Paid: $_____
Market Value: $_____

4

Bluebird Box
10035 • 4"
Issued: 1997 • Current
Price Paid: $_____
Market Value: $_____

5

Christmas Train Box
10192 • 4 ½"
Issued: 1997 • Current
Price Paid: $_____
Market Value: $_____

6

First Christmas Box
10191 • 4 ½"
Issued: 1997 • Current
Price Paid: $_____
Market Value: $_____

BOOKENDS

	Price Paid	Value of My Collection
1.		
2.		
3.		

BOXES

4.		
5.		
6.		
7.		
8.		
9.		
10.		

PENCIL TOTALS

7

Guardian Angel Box
10037 • 3 ½"
Issued: 1997 • Current
Price Paid: $_____
Market Value: $_____

8

Here Comes Trouble Box
10190 • 4 ¾"
Issued: 1997 • Current
Price Paid: $_____
Market Value: $_____

9

King Heart
"I Love You" Box
5850 • 7 ½"
Issued: 1991 • Suspended: 1992
Price Paid: $_____
Market Value: $_____

10

King Oval Cow Box
5860 • 10 ½"
Issued: 1991 • Suspended: 1992
Price Paid: $_____
Market Value: $_____

1

Kiss, Kiss Box
10034 • 4"
Issued: 1997 • Current
Price Paid: $____
Market Value: $_____

2

Medium Heart Cherub Box
5751 • 4"
Issued: 1991 • Suspended: 1992
Price Paid: $____
Market Value: $_____

3

Medium Octagonal Bunny Box
5752 • 4"
Issued: 1991 • Suspended: 1992
Price Paid: $____
Market Value: $_____

4

Medium Square "Speed Racer" Box
5750 • 4 ½"
Issued: 1991 • Suspended: 1992
Price Paid: $____
Market Value: $_____

5

Octagonal Ballerina Box
5700 • 3"
Issued: 1991 • Suspended: 1992
Price Paid: $____
Market Value: $_____

6

Queen Octagonal Cherub Box
5804 • 6 ½"
Issued: 1991 • Suspended: 1992
Price Paid: $____
Market Value: $_____

7

Queen Rectangle Cat Box
5800 • 6 ½"
Issued: 1991 • Suspended: 1992
Price Paid: $____
Market Value: $_____

8

Queen Rectangle Train Box
5803 • 7"
Issued: 1991 • Suspended: 1992
Price Paid: $____
Market Value: $_____

9

Queen Round Bears Box
5801 • 7"
Issued: 1991 • Suspended: 1992
Price Paid: $____
Market Value: $_____

10

Queen Square "You're Special" Box
5802 • 6"
Issued: 1991 • Suspended: 1992
Price Paid: $____
Market Value: $_____

BOXES

	Price Paid	Value of My Collection
1.		
2.		
3.		
4.		
5.		
6.		
7.		
8.		
9.		
10.		
	PENCIL TOTALS	

BOXES

1

Santa's Helper Box
10193 • 4 ¼"
Issued: 1997 • Current
Price Paid: $____
Market Value: $_____

2

Small Heart
"I Love You" Box
5701 • 3 ¼"
Issued: 1991 • Suspended: 1992
Price Paid: $____
Market Value: $_____

3

Small Rectangle
"Dicky Duck" Box
5703 • 3 ½"
Issued: 1991 • Suspended: 1992
Price Paid: $____
Market Value: $_____

4

Small Square
Dinosaur Box
5702 • 3"
Issued: 1991 • Suspended: 1992
Price Paid: $____
Market Value: $_____

5

Tiny Dancer Box
10036 • 4 ¼"
Issued: 1997 • Current
Price Paid: $____
Market Value: $_____

6

Chill Chaser
(Early Release - Fall 1997)
10117 • 4 ½"
Issued: TBA • Current
Price Paid: $____
Market Value: $_____

BOXES

	Price Paid	Value of My Collection
1.		
2.		
3.		
4.		
5.		

CANDLE & VOTIVE HOLDERS

6.		
7.		
8.		
9.		
10.		

PENCIL TOTALS

7

Dream Street
10118 • 5 ¼"
Issued: 1997 • Current
Price Paid: $____
Market Value: $_____

8

Fireside Fun
DK041 • 3"
Issued: 1996 • Current
Price Paid: $____
Market Value: $_____

9

Large Candle Holder #1
DC138 • 6"
Issued: 1993 • Retired: 1994
Price Paid: $____
Market Value: $_____

10

Large Candle Holder #2
DC139 • 6"
Issued: 1993 • Retired: 1994
Price Paid: $____
Market Value: $_____

1

Light My Way
10122 • 3 ¾″
Issued: 1997 • Current
Price Paid: $____
Market Value: $____

2

Pumpkin Capers
10201 • 3 ½″
Issued: 1997 • Current
Price Paid: $____
Market Value: $____

3

Pumpkin Pretender
10202 • 3 ¼″
Issued: 1997 • Current
Price Paid: $____
Market Value: $____

4

Small Candle Holder #1
DC136 • 2 ½″
Issued: 1993 • Suspended: 1996
Price Paid: $____
Market Value: $____

5

Small Candle Holder #1
DX136 • 2 ½″
Issued: 1994 • Ret./Susp.: 1997
Price Paid: $____
Market Value: $____

6

Small Candle Holder #2
DC137 • 2 ½″
Issued: 1993 • Suspended: 1996
Price Paid: $____
Market Value: $____

7

Small Candle Holder #2
DX137 • 2 ½″
Issued: 1994 • Ret./Susp.: 1997
Price Paid: $____
Market Value: $____

8

Star Of Wonder
10145 • 3 ½″
Issued: 1997 • Retired: 1997
Price Paid: $____
Market Value: $____

9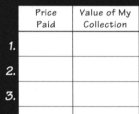

Star Of Wonder
10148 • 3″
Issued: 1997 • Retired: 1997
Price Paid: $____
Market Value: $____

10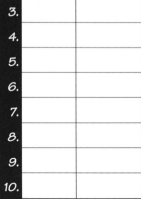

Strange Brew
10200 • 4 ¼″
Issued: 1997 • Current
Price Paid: $____
Market Value: $____

CANDLE & VOTIVE HOLDERS

	Price Paid	Value of My Collection
1.		
2.		
3.		
4.		
5.		
6.		
7.		
8.		
9.		
10.		
PENCIL TOTALS		

CANDLE & VOTIVE HOLDERS

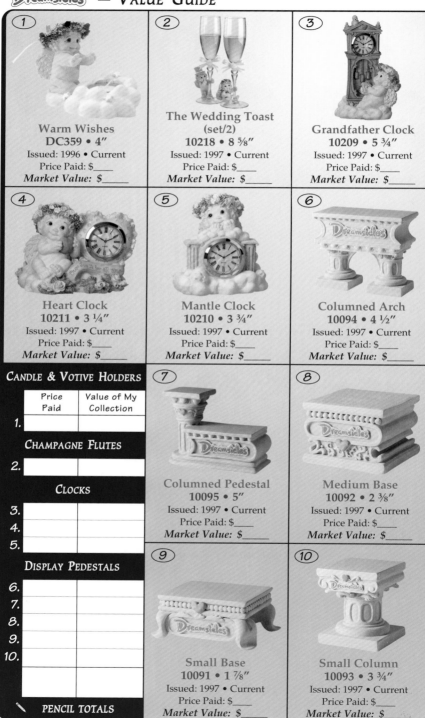

Dreamsicles™ — VALUE GUIDE

① Warm Wishes
DC359 • 4"
Issued: 1996 • Current
Price Paid: $____
Market Value: $_____

② The Wedding Toast
(set/2)
10218 • 8 ⅝"
Issued: 1997 • Current
Price Paid: $____
Market Value: $_____

③ Grandfather Clock
10209 • 5 ¾"
Issued: 1997 • Current
Price Paid: $____
Market Value: $_____

④ Heart Clock
10211 • 3 ¼"
Issued: 1997 • Current
Price Paid: $____
Market Value: $_____

⑤ Mantle Clock
10210 • 3 ¾"
Issued: 1997 • Current
Price Paid: $____
Market Value: $_____

⑥ Columned Arch
10094 • 4 ½"
Issued: 1997 • Current
Price Paid: $____
Market Value: $_____

⑦ Columned Pedestal
10095 • 5"
Issued: 1997 • Current
Price Paid: $____
Market Value: $_____

⑧ Medium Base
10092 • 2 ⅜"
Issued: 1997 • Current
Price Paid: $____
Market Value: $_____

⑨ Small Base
10091 • 1 ⅞"
Issued: 1997 • Current
Price Paid: $____
Market Value: $_____

⑩ Small Column
10093 • 3 ¾"
Issued: 1997 • Current
Price Paid: $____
Market Value: $_____

CANDLE & VOTIVE HOLDERS

	Price Paid	Value of My Collection
1.		

CHAMPAGNE FLUTES

2.		

CLOCKS

3.		
4.		
5.		

DISPLAY PEDESTALS

6.		
7.		
8.		
9.		
10.		

PENCIL TOTALS

1 New

Heaven's Little Helper Egg
10390 • 4 ½"
Issued: 1998 • Current
Price Paid: $____
Market Value: $____

2 New

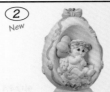

Join The Fun Egg
10394 • 4 ½"
Issued: 1998 • Current
Price Paid: $____
Market Value: $____

3 New

Merry-Go-Round Egg
10391 • 4 ½"
Issued: 1998 • Current
Price Paid: $____
Market Value: $____

4 New

Snuggle Blanket Egg
10393 • 4 ½"
Issued: 1998 • Current
Price Paid: $____
Market Value: $____

5 New

Sweethearts Egg
10392 • 4 ½"
Issued: 1998 • Current
Price Paid: $____
Market Value: $____

6

Balloons Frame
DF005 • 3 ½
Issued: 1993 • Suspended: 1994
Price Paid: $____
Market Value: $____

7

Column Picture Frame
10224 • 7"
Issued: 1997 • Current
Price Paid: $____
Market Value: $____

8

Heart Picture Frame
10225 • 4 ½"
Issued: 1997 • Current
Price Paid: $____
Market Value: $____

9

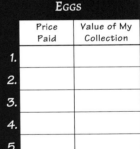

Kite Frame
DF006 • 3 ½"
Issued: 1993 • Suspended: 1994
Price Paid: $____
Market Value: $____

10

Large Heart Frame
DF002 • 4"
Issued: 1993 • Suspended: 1994
Price Paid: $____
Market Value: $____

EGGS	Price Paid	Value of My Collection
1.		
2.		
3.		
4.		
5.		

FRAMES		
6.		
7.		
8.		
9.		
10.		
PENCIL TOTALS		

EGGS/FRAMES

Dreamsicles™ — Value Guide

1
Oval Frame
DF004 • 3 ⅞"
Issued: 1993 • Suspended: 1994
Price Paid: $____
Market Value: $_____

2
Small Heart Frame
DF001 • 3 ⅜"
Issued: 1993 • Suspended: 1994
Price Paid: $____
Market Value: $_____

3
Star Frame
DF003 • 3 ⅛"
Issued: 1993 • Suspended: 1994
Price Paid: $____
Market Value: $_____

4
Surrounded By Love Frame
10222 • 6 ¼"
Issued: 1997 • Current
Price Paid: $____
Market Value: $_____

5
Baby's First
10136 • 3"
Issued: 1997 • Current
Price Paid: $____
Market Value: $_____

6
Bear
DX274 • 2 ½"
Issued: 1991 • Suspended: 1993
Price Paid: $____
Market Value: $_____

FRAMES

	Price Paid	Value of My Collection
1.		
2.		
3.		
4.		

ORNAMENTS

5.		
6.		
7.		
8.		
9.		
10.		

PENCIL TOTALS

7
Bunny
DX270 • 2 ½"
Issued: 1991 • Suspended: 1993
Price Paid: $____
Market Value: $_____

8
Cherub Facing Bunny
DX283 • 2"
Issued: 1994 • Current
Price Paid: $____
Market Value: $_____

9
Cherub On Cloud
DX263 • 2 ½"
Issued: 1991 • Suspended: 1993
Price Paid: $____
Market Value: $_____

10
Cherub With Baby
DX286 • 2"
Issued: 1994 • Current
Price Paid: $____
Market Value: $_____

1

Cherub With Bear
DX282 • 2"
Issued: 1994 • Current
Price Paid: $____
Market Value: $____

2

Cherub With Bird
DX287 • 2"
Issued: 1994 • Current
Price Paid: $____
Market Value: $____

3

Cherub With Book
DX280 • 2"
Issued: 1994 • Current
Price Paid: $____
Market Value: $____

4

Cherub With Bunny
DX288 • 2"
Issued: 1994 • Current
Price Paid: $____
Market Value: $____

5

Cherub With Drum
DX281 • 2"
Issued: 1994 • Current
Price Paid: $____
Market Value: $____

6

Cherub With Flute
DX285 • 2"
Issued: 1994 • Current
Price Paid: $____
Market Value: $____

7

Cherub With Horn
DX289 • 2"
Issued: 1994 • Current
Price Paid: $____
Market Value: $____

8

Cherub With Moon
DX260 • 2 ½"
Issued: 1991 • Suspended: 1993
Price Paid: $____
Market Value: $____

9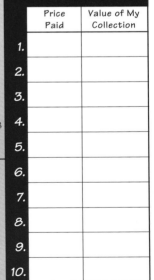

Cherub With Star
DX262 • 2 ½"
Issued: 1991 • Suspended: 1993
Price Paid: $____
Market Value: $____

10

Eager To Please
DX295 • 2 ⅛"
Issued: 1995 • Current
Price Paid: $____
Market Value: $____

ORNAMENTS

	Price Paid	Value of My Collection
1.		
2.		
3.		
4.		
5.		
6.		
7.		
8.		
9.		
10.		
	PENCIL TOTALS	

ORNAMENTS

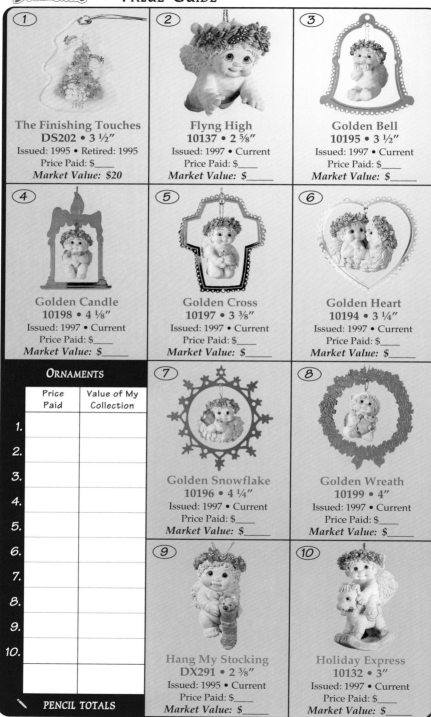

Dreamsicles™ — VALUE GUIDE

①

The Finishing Touches
DS202 • 3 ½"
Issued: 1995 • Retired: 1995
Price Paid: $____
Market Value: $20

②

Flyng High
10137 • 2 ⅝"
Issued: 1997 • Current
Price Paid: $____
Market Value: $____

③

Golden Bell
10195 • 3 ½"
Issued: 1997 • Current
Price Paid: $____
Market Value: $____

④

Golden Candle
10198 • 4 ⅛"
Issued: 1997 • Current
Price Paid: $____
Market Value: $____

⑤

Golden Cross
10197 • 3 ⅜"
Issued: 1997 • Current
Price Paid: $____
Market Value: $____

⑥

Golden Heart
10194 • 3 ¼"
Issued: 1997 • Current
Price Paid: $____
Market Value: $____

ORNAMENTS

	Price Paid	Value of My Collection
1.		
2.		
3.		
4.		
5.		
6.		
7.		
8.		
9.		
10.		

PENCIL TOTALS

⑦

Golden Snowflake
10196 • 4 ¼"
Issued: 1997 • Current
Price Paid: $____
Market Value: $____

⑧

Golden Wreath
10199 • 4"
Issued: 1997 • Current
Price Paid: $____
Market Value: $____

⑨

Hang My Stocking
DX291 • 2 ⅜"
Issued: 1995 • Current
Price Paid: $____
Market Value: $____

⑩

Holiday Express
10132 • 3"
Issued: 1997 • Current
Price Paid: $____
Market Value: $____

1

Holiday Hugs
10134 • 2 ¼"
Issued: 1997 • Current
Price Paid: $____
Market Value: $____

2

I Can Read
DX297 • 1 ¾"
Issued: 1995 • Current
Price Paid: $____
Market Value: $____

3

Just For You
10135 • 2 ⅝"
Issued: 1997 • Current
Price Paid: $____
Market Value: $____

4

Kiss, Kiss
DX298 • 1 ⅞"
Issued: 1995 • Current
Price Paid: $____
Market Value: $____

5

Lamb
DX275 • 2 ½"
Issued: 1991 • Suspended: 1993
Price Paid: $____
Market Value: $____

6

Nativity Ornament Set
(set/6)
DX466 • various
Issued: 1996 • Current
Price Paid: $____
Market Value: $____

7

Piggy
DX271 • 2 ½"
Issued: 1991 • Suspended: 1993
Price Paid: $____
Market Value: $____

8

Piggy Back Kitty
DX284 • 2"
Issued: 1994 • Current
Price Paid: $____
Market Value: $____

9

Poinsettia
DX292 • 1 ¾"
Issued: 1995 • Current
Price Paid: $____
Market Value: $____

10

Praying Cherub
DX261 • 2 ½"
Issued: 1991 • Suspended: 1993
Price Paid: $____
Market Value: $____

ORNAMENTS

	Price Paid	Value of My Collection
1.		
2.		
3.		
4.		
5.		
6.		
7.		
8.		
9.		
10.		

PENCIL TOTALS

ORNAMENTS

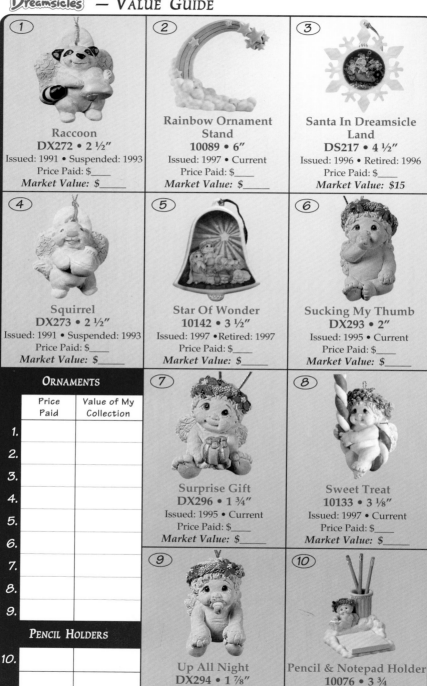

1

Raccoon
DX272 • 2 ½″
Issued: 1991 • Suspended: 1993
Price Paid: $____
Market Value: $_____

2

Rainbow Ornament Stand
10089 • 6″
Issued: 1997 • Current
Price Paid: $____
Market Value: $_____

3

Santa In Dreamsicle Land
DS217 • 4 ½″
Issued: 1996 • Retired: 1996
Price Paid: $____
Market Value: $15

4

Squirrel
DX273 • 2 ½″
Issued: 1991 • Suspended: 1993
Price Paid: $____
Market Value: $_____

5

Star Of Wonder
10142 • 3 ½″
Issued: 1997 •Retired: 1997
Price Paid: $____
Market Value: $_____

6

Sucking My Thumb
DX293 • 2″
Issued: 1995 • Current
Price Paid: $____
Market Value: $_____

Ornaments

	Price Paid	Value of My Collection
1.		
2.		
3.		
4.		
5.		
6.		
7.		
8.		
9.		

Pencil Holders

10.		

PENCIL TOTALS

7

Surprise Gift
DX296 • 1 ¾″
Issued: 1995 • Current
Price Paid: $____
Market Value: $_____

8

Sweet Treat
10133 • 3 ⅛″
Issued: 1997 • Current
Price Paid: $____
Market Value: $_____

9

Up All Night
DX294 • 1 ⅞″
Issued: 1995 • Current
Price Paid: $____
Market Value: $_____

10

Pencil & Notepad Holder
10076 • 3 ¾
Issued: 1997 • Current
Price Paid: $____
Market Value: $_____

①

Bedtime Prayer
10214 • 9 ¼"
Issued: 1997 • Current
Price Paid: $_____
Market Value: $_____

②

Bless This House
DC177 • 5"
Issued: 1994 • Current
Price Paid: $_____
Market Value: $_____

③

Bunny Wall Plaque
5018 • 11 ½"
Issued: 1992 • Suspended: 1992
Price Paid: $_____
Market Value: $_____

④

Bunny Wall Plaque
5019 • 12 ½"
Issued: 1992 • Suspended: 1992
Price Paid: $_____
Market Value: $_____

⑤

Cherub Wall Plaque
5130 • 7"
Issued: 1992 • Suspended: 1992
Price Paid: $_____
Market Value: $_____

⑥

Cherub Wall Plaque
5131 • 7"
Issued: 1992 • Suspended: 1992
Price Paid: $_____
Market Value: $_____

⑦

Heavenly Harp
10215 • 8 ¼"
Issued: 1997 • Current
Price Paid: $_____
Market Value: $_____

⑧

Join The Fun
10212 • 10 ½"
Issued: 1997 • Current
Price Paid: $_____
Market Value: $_____

⑨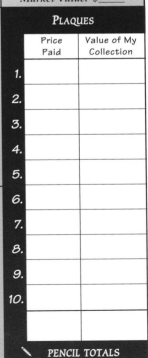

Moonbeams
10213 • 11"
Issued: 1997 • Current
Price Paid: $_____
Market Value: $_____

⑩

Snuggle Blanket
10216 • 9"
Issued: 1997 • Current
Price Paid: $_____
Market Value: $_____

PLAQUES	Price Paid	Value of My Collection
1.		
2.		
3.		
4.		
5.		
6.		
7.		
8.		
9.		
10.		
PENCIL TOTALS		

PLAQUES

Dreamsicles™ — VALUE GUIDE

1 **Starburst**
10217 • 10"
Issued: 1997 • Current
Price Paid: $____
Market Value: $____

2 **Watching Over You**
DC176 • 5"
Issued: 1994 • Current
Price Paid: $____
Market Value: $____

3 **The Finishing Touches**
DS200 • 8 ¼"
Issued: 1995 • Retired: 1995
Price Paid: $____
Market Value: $40

4 **Santa In Dreamsicle Land**
DS215 • 8 ¼"
Issued: 1996 • Retired: 1996
Price Paid: $____
Market Value: $40

5 **Star Of Wonder**
10144 • 8"
Issued: 1997 • Retired: 1997
Price Paid: $____
Market Value: $____

6 **Cherub Bowl - Hearts**
DC160 • 4"
Issued: 1994 • Ret./Susp.: 1997
Price Paid: $____
Market Value: $____

7 **Cherub Bowl - Stars**
DC161 • 4"
Issued: 1994 • Suspended: 1996
Price Paid: $____
Market Value: $40

8 **Potpourri Bunnies**
DA117 • 4 ½"
Issued: 1994 • Suspended: 1996
Price Paid: $____
Market Value: $20

9 **Potpourri Pals**
DA118 • 3 ½"
Issued: 1994 • Suspended: 1996
Price Paid: $____
Market Value: $20

PLAQUES

	Price Paid	Value of My Collection
1.		
2.		

PLATES

3.		
4.		
5.		

POTPOURRI HOLDERS

6.		
7.		
8.		
9.		

✎ **PENCIL TOTALS**

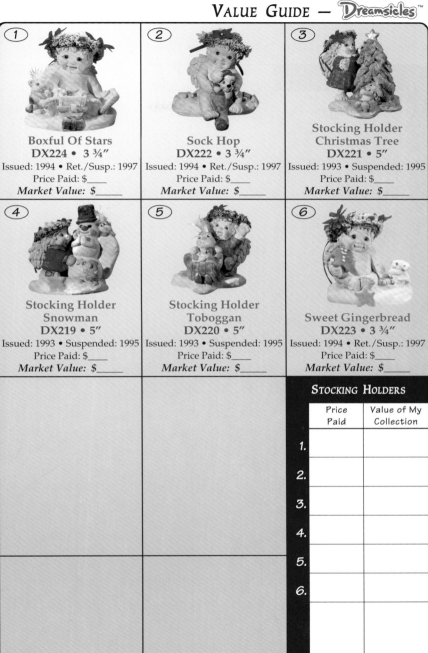

1 Boxful Of Stars
DX224 • 3 ¾"
Issued: 1994 • Ret./Susp.: 1997
Price Paid: $____
Market Value: $_____

2 Sock Hop
DX222 • 3 ¾"
Issued: 1994 • Ret./Susp.: 1997
Price Paid: $____
Market Value: $_____

3 Stocking Holder
Christmas Tree
DX221 • 5"
Issued: 1993 • Suspended: 1995
Price Paid: $____
Market Value: $_____

4 Stocking Holder
Snowman
DX219 • 5"
Issued: 1993 • Suspended: 1995
Price Paid: $____
Market Value: $_____

5 Stocking Holder
Toboggan
DX220 • 5"
Issued: 1993 • Suspended: 1995
Price Paid: $____
Market Value: $_____

6 Sweet Gingerbread
DX223 • 3 ¾"
Issued: 1994 • Ret./Susp.: 1997
Price Paid: $____
Market Value: $_____

STOCKING HOLDERS		
	Price Paid	Value of My Collection
1.		
2.		
3.		
4.		
5.		
6.		
PENCIL TOTALS		

STOCKING HOLDERS

Use these pages to record future Dreamsicles releases.

DREAMSICLES	Item Number	Size	Status	Market Value	Price Paid	Value of My Collection
					PENCIL TOTALS	
					Price Paid	Market Value

Use these pages to record future Dreamsicles releases.

DREAMSICLES	Item Number	Size	Status	Market Value	Price Paid	Value of My Collection
		PENCIL TOTALS			Price Paid	Market Value

Use these pages to record future Dreamsicles releases.

Dreamsicles	Item Number	Size	Status	Market Value	Price Paid	Value of My Collection
			PENCIL TOTALS			
					Price Paid	Market Value

Total Value Of My Collection

Record the value of your collection here by adding the pencil totals from the bottom of each Value Guide page.

DREAMSICLES	Price Paid	Market Value
Page 27		
Page 28		
Page 29		
Page 30		
Page 31		
Page 32		
Page 33		
Page 34		
Page 35		
Page 36		
Page 37		
Page 38		
Page 39		
Page 40		
Page 41		
Page 42		
Page 43		
Page 44		
Page 45		
Page 46		
Page 47		
Page 48		
Page 49		
Page 50		
Page 51		
TOTAL		

DREAMSICLES	Price Paid	Market Value
Page 52		
Page 53		
Page 54		
Page 55		
Page 56		
Page 57		
Page 58		
Page 59		
Page 60		
Page 61		
Page 62		
Page 63		
Page 64		
Page 65		
Page 66		
Page 67		
Page 68		
Page 69		
Page 70		
Page 71		
Page 72		
Page 73		
Page 74		
Page 75		
Page 76		
TOTAL		

PAGE SUBTOTALS		
	PRICE PAID	MARKET VALUE

Total Value Of My Collection

*Record the value of your collection here by adding the pencil totals
from the bottom of each Value Guide page.*

DREAMSICLES	Price Paid	Market Value
Page 77		
Page 78		
Page 79		
Page 80		
Page 81		
Page 82		
Page 83		
Page 84		
Page 85		
Page 86		
Page 87		
Page 88		
Page 89		
Page 90		
Page 91		
Page 92		
Page 93		
Page 94		
Page 95		
Page 96		
Page 97		
Page 98		
Page 99		
Page 100		
Page 101		
TOTAL		

DREAMSICLES	Price Paid	Market Value
Page 102		
Page 103		
Page 104		
Page 105		
Page 106		
Page 107		
Page 108		
Page 109		
Page 110		
Page 111		
Page 112		
Page 113		
Page 114		
Page 115		
Page 116		
Page 117		
Page 118		
Page 119		
Page 120		
Page 121		
Page 122		
Page 123		
Page 124		
Page 125		
Page 126		
TOTAL		

GRAND TOTALS		
	PRICE PAID	MARKET VALUE

Wedding

Left to Right: The Wedding March (#10121), Hand In Hand (#DC431), It's Your Day (#10220), The Happy Couple (#10219), Wedding Rehearsal (#DC134).

Baby

Left to Right: Baby Boom (#10045), Counting Sheep (#DC417), Hushaby Baby (#DC303), New Beginnings (#10251), First Born (#10130), Mother's Helper (#10141).

Anniversary

Left to Right: Sign Of Love (#10158), All My Lovin' (#DC313), Sweethearts (#DC200).

Dreamsicles Gift Ideas

Left to Right: Birthday Wishes (#10166), Birthday Fun (#10323), Pint-Sized Parade (#DC323),
It's Your Birthday (#DC304), Making A Cake (#DC418).

Left to Right: Forever Friends (#10276), Friendship Cherubs (#DC175), Best Friends (#DC342), We're
Best Friends (#DC715), You've Got A Friend (#DC170).

Left to Right: Sealed With A Kiss (#DC429), Here's My Heart (#10260), I Love You (#10271),
Please Be Mine (#10259), For My Valentine (#DK010).

Easter

Left to Right: Eggstra Special (#10063), Bunny Power (#10067), Easter Artist (#10325), Easter Basket (#10322), Baby Bunny (#10065), Easter Morning (#DC312).

Mother's Day

Left to Right: Mom's The Best (#DC428), From The Heart (#10116), A Kiss For Momma (#DC402), I Love Mommy (#DC226), Mom's Garden (#10328), Love You, Mom (#DK011).

Graduation

Left to Right: Graduation Day (#DC219), Happy Graduate (#DC705), The Graduate (#DC135).

Secondary Market Overview

The Dreamsicles collection has followed an interesting path toward "collectible" status. Cast Art Industries introduced Dreamsicles in 1991 and, from the beginning, the adorable cherubs sold very well in retail stores. Many people were buying Dreamsicles as decorating accessories or gifts for different occasions. The Dreamsicles collection was a hit!

In the early days, there wasn't a lot of information available to Dreamsicles fans to help them build their collections. The first Dreamsicles pieces were issued without official names (Cast Art assigned them names after they realized the popularity of their new gift line). Identifying stickers with the name and stock number were added to the bottoms of the figurines in the summer of 1994. Previously, retailers had difficulty matching boxes with the correct figurines, so early pieces often did not come in the correct box. With so many pieces and so much difficulty in identifying the pieces, there weren't many people scrambling to "collect them all."

Cast Art began issuing limited edition pieces in 1992 and this was the first hint that Dreamsicles might become a "collectible." The early limited editions sold out within a year of their release and a 1993 limited edition figurine, "The Flying Lesson" became the fastest-selling Dreamsicles piece up to that point. When Cast Art introduced the Dreamsicles Club for collectors in 1993, Dreamsicles enthusiasts finally had a resource to help them unite with other collectors and learn more about their collection.

The limited edition figurines have become the focal point for the growing Dreamsicles secondary market, which is still in its early stages of development. Not all retired and suspended Dreamsicles have seen activity on the secondary market, but this is likely to increase over time as legions of new Dreamsicles fans join the difficult hunt for earlier pieces. The Collector's Value Guide™, with information and full-color pictures on every Dreamsicles piece since their introduction, is an essential tool for collectors looking to learn more about their Dreamsicles collection and its potential secondary market value.

Secondary Market Overview

1. Where is the secondary market?

There are various ways in which collectors can buy and sell pieces on the secondary market. The easiest way to reach other collectors is through a *secondary market exchange service*. Collectors list the pieces they wish to buy or sell with the exchange service, which then publishes a list of the pieces and the asking price. The exchange acts as the middleman in the transaction for a commission on each completed sale (usually between 10% and 20%). One benefit to using an exchange is that you can easily reach collectors all over the country. Most exchange listings are published monthly and may require a subscription or membership fee. A few exchanges generate daily listings, which collectors can call for and receive by mail. There also are exchange services that sell *their own* pieces and not those of collectors; there would be no commission in these cases.

Many newsletters and magazines feature their own "swap & sell" sections, which operate in much the same way as the exchange services. Some collectors place *classified advertisements* in their local newspapers (under Antiques/Collectibles), but it may take longer to find or sell pieces this way because newspapers reach a general readership and are not focused specifically on collectors. Dreamsicles Club members can contact other collectors directly by placing a notice of the pieces they are looking for in the "Wish List" section of *The ClubHouse* newsletter, which is published four times a year.

Although most *retailers* aren't actively involved in the secondary market, they can often be a good source of information or advice for collectors. For example, if a collector is looking to sell some pieces, his or her local retailer may be able to direct them to another collector looking to buy pieces. Retailers may also sponsor secondary market collector shows as a service to their customers. Local and regional collector clubs also sponsor secondary market events.

The newest and perhaps most exciting secondary market source is the *Internet* via home computer. Here, collectors can find information about Dreamsicles without leaving their homes! Some of the websites

COLLECTOR'S
VALUE GUIDE™

Secondary Market Overview

and entries are retail stores that carry Dreamsicles products, while others are bulletin boards where collectors share information and can trade, buy and sell pieces. The virtue of these on-line price listings is that they can be updated immediately and can be used for quick sales or trades. The best way to get Dreamsicles information on the Internet is to use a search function. You may want to search for specific essential phrases, such as "Dreamsicles *and* collectibles" or "Dreamsicles *and* cherubs *and* secondary." These searches will lead you to retailers, collectors, publishers and secondary market dealers who can help you find the Dreamsicles information you're looking for.

2. How does the secondary market work?

Limited editions, Club pieces and special event pieces frequently command the highest prices on the Dreamsicles secondary market. However, not all limited editions are highly coveted; it all depends upon how many pieces were made and how popular it is with collectors. The same goes for open stock pieces that are retired. As a general rule, prices tend to increase over the years as fewer pieces are available on the secondary market. Pieces produced for only two or three years will typically have a higher secondary market value than those in production for a greater number of years.

The value of any piece is dependent upon its condition, a damaged piece being less valuable. Many secondary market listings use notations such as "factory flaw" or "chipped," conditions that will decrease the value of a piece on the secondary market. Sometimes pieces suffer damage in the course of being displayed. Common blemishes include stray wisps of paint, water damage, scrapes and chips. Always remember to inspect your pieces carefully whether you're buying or selling, and be aware that some pieces on the secondary market have been repaired or restored. There's nothing wrong with buying a restored piece, as long as you know that it has been repaired and you understand that its resale value will be decreased.

COLLECTOR'S
VALUE GUIDE™

Secondary Market Overview

Whether you're buying or selling on the secondary market, an important factor to consider is the original packaging of the pieces. In the "real world," a box is just a box; but in the world of collectibles, boxes and packing sleeves take on an important new meaning. Not only are the boxes perfect for storing and protecting your pieces, but many collectors will consider a piece that is sold without its original packaging to be "incomplete." These pieces will generally command a lower price on the secondary market. Inside packaging (tissue paper, foam, etc.) usually varies from piece to piece and doesn't usually affect the value.

Sales on the secondary market typically slow down in the summer and pick up as the holidays approach. Because demand for pieces increases later in the year, prices generally increase as well, so you may prefer to sell late in the year and buy earlier in the year. There really is no "right" or "wrong" time to buy or sell; it all depends on how much you're willing to pay for a piece you want to add to your collection or how much it will take for you to part with one of your pieces.

Lastly, it's important to remember that not every piece will soar in value, so if your sole reason to collect Dreamsicles figurines is for the investment, you may be disappointed. You're much better off doing it for the fun!

Variations

When something becomes a "collectible," whether it's stamps, baseball cards or figurines, there is often a lot of excitement about the possibility of variations. While Cast Art maintains high standards for uniformity and excellence in manufacturing Dreamsicles, a good deal of the work is handcrafted, so there are bound to be slight variations from piece to piece. Among the more notable variations are color changes, design changes and small errors, such as misspellings.

Over the years, several Dreamsicles pieces have had slight color modifications. In fact, in 1997, Cast Art revised 40 existing Dreamsicles, replacing the original hues with softer, more subdued colors. For example, "The Graduate" moved from a deep blue robe to a pastel gown, while "Sugarfoot," originally dressed in bright colors and shod in dark brown cowboy boots was changed to pale blues and tans.

Some Dreamsicles figurines have been redesigned, particularly those figurines that were originally issued as "early releases" at a limited number of selected retailers, then subsequently released into the general line. Several examples of redesigned figurines are listed below.

1995 Dreamsicles Day Event Figurine (#DC075) & Signing Figurine (#DC074): The "1995 Dreamsicles Day Event Figurine" depicted a cherub seated on a cloud, holding a pen and scroll, with the words "Dreamsicles Day 1995." A second version, "Signing Figurine" was released with a blank scroll and could be signed by Dreamsicles artist Kristin Haynes at several International Collectible Expositions.

1995
Dreamsicles Day
Event Figurine

Signing
Figurine

The Good Book (#DC361): "The Good Book" was first introduced in the Fall of 1996 as an early release. When the figurine was released into the general line the following June, the color of the Bible had changed from light tan to gray.

The Good Book
(tan bible)

The Good Book
(gray bible)

Making Memories (#HC381 & #10096): The *Heavenly Classics* figurine "Making Memories" was an early release through the National Association of Limited Edition Dealers (N.A.L.E.D.) as #HC381. The piece was redesigned with a sleeker-winged classical angel painted in slightly deeper colors before it was issued into the general line as #10096.

Making Memories   Making Memories (#10096)

Star Power (#10128) & Stardust (#10385): "Star Power" was an early release in the Fall of 1997. When released into the general line in 1998, it was renamed "Stardust" and featured only one star as opposed to a cluster of stars in the original version.

Star Power   Stardust

Together Again (#10246) & Humpty Dumpty (#10372): "Together Again," an early release in 1997, featured a cherub sitting next to nursery rhyme character Humpty Dumpty. The figurine was released to the general line in 1998 as "Humpty Dumpty." This version has a new base featuring grass and flowers, and a sculpted wreath on the cherub.

Together Again   Humpty Dumpty

The following two figurines were not redesigned, but a limited number of pieces were originally released with spelling errors.

Poetry In Motion (#DC113): During the early production of this figurine, "Poetry" was misspelled as "Potery" on the nameplate. Cast Art estimates that about 80 of these pieces were shipped before the error was caught and corrected. "Poetry In Motion" was retired in 1997.

Rainbow's End (#DC311): When Rainbow's End was first produced in 1995, "Rainbow" was misspelled as "Ranibow" on the label that appears on the bottom of the figurine. About 5,000 were shipped before the error was corrected by Cast Art.

It's too early to tell how valuable Dreamsicles variations may become on the secondary market, but as time goes on, these early variations are likely to be considered the "rarest of the rare."

Insuring Your Collection

While the pieces in your collection hold sentimental value, they also have a dollar value. When you add up each purchase, you may find that you've invested quite a bit putting your collection together. Then, when you look at the secondary market values and figure out what it would cost to replace pieces in your collection, you might decide you want to insure your collection just as you insure the other valuables in your home. There are three steps to determining whether you should insure your collection: *knowing your coverage, documenting the contents and value of your collection* and *weighing the risk.*

1. Know your coverage

Collectibles are considered part of the contents of a house and as such, they are typically included in homeowners or renters insurance policies. Ask your agent about the types of loss or damage your policy covers and what it doesn't cover. A standard policy covers household contents for damage or loss from perils such as fire, hurricanes and theft. Common exclusions include earthquakes, floods and breakage through routine handling. In addition to determining the types of loss that are covered, ask your agent about the dollar value that would be paid out in the event that you have to file a claim. The amount paid out will vary based on the type of coverage you have. Today, most insurance policies are written at replacement value which would provide enough money to replace a lost or damaged collection. Replacement value policies pay out the amount needed to actually replace the items (minus the deductible), which is important for collectibles because they appreciate in value.

2. Document the contents and value of your collection

In order to determine how much coverage you need, you must first document your collection to calculate how much it would cost to replace your pieces. There are many ways to document your collection, from a simple listing to hiring an appraiser, but you should check with your insurance agent first to find out what records the insurance company will accept in the event of a loss. Generally, companies want to see proof that you own particular pieces as well as proof of their value.

COLLECTOR'S
VALUE GUIDE™

Insuring Your Collection

Two of the best forms of documentation are receipts and a "schedule." The schedule is a listing of each piece in your collection and should include the purchase date, price paid, where you purchased the piece, special markings and secondary market value. Some companies will accept a reputable secondary market guide, such as the Collector's Value Guide, for pricing.

Two features of the Collector's Value Guide are designed to aid you if you should decide to insure your collection. The Value Guide section includes 1998 secondary market prices to help you determine the replacement value of your pieces. Keep in mind that your insurance carrier may want to distinguish between items which are available through normal retail outlets versus pieces which are no longer available (i.e., retired or suspended). It makes sense to list or "schedule" your valuable retired pieces on your policy, just as you would for jewelry and other important valuables.

To ensure proper coverage, it is important that your agent understands secondary market values. If you have particularly valuable pieces or if you have an extensive collection, you should note that the more valuable the item, the more demanding the insurance company will be for industry-accepted valuation. In some cases, the carrier may even want a professional appraisal. For appraisers in your area, contact the American Society of Appraisers at 1-800-ASA-VALU.

Photographs and video footage of your collection are a good back-up in case of an unforeseen problem with your claim. Snapshots and video should record closeup views of the piece (including the bottoms) and show any production marks or artist signatures. Print two sets of photographs; store one set in your home and give the second set to a friend or put them in a safe deposit box.

3. Weigh the risk

After you calculate the replacement cost of your collection, you can determine if you have adequate insurance to cover any losses. To do this, add the estimated value of your home furnishings to the value of your

COLLECTOR'S
VALUE GUIDE™

collectibles (as totaled in this book) and consult your insurance policy for the amount of coverage. Compare the total value of the contents of your home to the dollar amount you would be paid in the event that you had to file a claim.

If you find your policy does not provide enough coverage, you can purchase additional insurance for your collectibles. This can be done by adding a "Personal Articles Floater" (PAF) or a "Fine Arts Floater" or "rider" to your homeowners policy which provides broader coverage and insures your collection for a specific dollar amount. Another option is to purchase a separate policy specifically for collectibles from a specialized insurance provider. One such company is American Collectors Insurance, Inc. in Cherry Hill, New Jersey, which offers coverage for a wide variety of collectibles, from figurines to dolls to memorabilia. A sample application form is shown here. You can reach American Collectors Insurance at: 1-800-257-5758.

Apply Now For A Collectibles Insurance Policy

COLLECTIBLES INSURANCE POLICY APPLICATION

Underwritten by American Bankers Insurance Company of Florida

Name	Occupation	Birth Date / /
Street Address	City	State	Zip
Spouse's Name	(Area Code) Telephone No.
Describe Residence: ❑ Apartment ❑ Single Family Home ❑ Other ____
Insured Value of Residence $	Insurance Company
Type of Collection(s)	Total Value of Collection(s) $

Is your collection ever stored/displayed outside of your residence address? .... ❑ YES ❑ NO
Have you had a homeowner's loss/claim on your collection within the past 3 years? ❑ YES ❑ NO
If you answered YES to either question, please explain:____

Does your residence have smoke detectors? .... ❑ YES ❑ NO
Does your residence have a fire/burglary security system? .... ❑ YES ❑ NO
If YES, by ____ ❑ Local Alarm ❑ Central Station
If NO, my house is protected when no one is home by: ____

From your residence, what is the distance:
to the nearest fire hydrant? .... ____ FEET
to the nearest fire department? .... ____ MILES
to the nearest police department? .... ____ MILES
If your residence is located more than 1000 feet from a fire hydrant, please answer the following:
1. Do you have a year-round water-source near your home (e.g. swimming pool, pond, etc.)? If yes, please describe: ____
What is the approximate distance of water source to residence? ____
2. Your local fire department is. ____ ❑ Paid ❑ Volunteer

Please calculate your annual premium on the back of this form. If paying by VISA or MASTERCARD, you will need to supply your account information below.

Account # ____ Expiration Date: ____ / ____

Tear this completed application off along perforation. Fold in half so that this edge meets the top edge. Then tape edges together. If you plan to pay with check or money order, please enclose and tape all edges. Remember to sign other side!

sample application

As with all insurance, you must weigh the risk of loss against the cost of additional coverage.

Kristin Haynes Biography

Kristin Haynes' creative talents were nurtured from the day she was born. Her fondest memories of her childhood years in Utah are of drawing. Her mother, watercolorist Abbie Whitney, supplied Kristin and her three siblings with paper, pencils, and the freedom to use their imagination. In her teens, Kristin expanded her artistic interests by creating crafts and caroling figures with her family. Kristin met her husband Scott while both were attending the University of Utah (she specialized in sculpture) and the couple moved to California in 1978.

While raising her three children – Harmony, Dustin and Patrick – Kristin began experimenting with sculptures of small animals and cherubs. She began selling her creations on weekends at local arts and crafts fairs. Trying to juggle family responsibilities with the growing popularity of her sculptures, she soon realized she needed help in keeping up with the demand. She presented her sculptures to several manufacturers and received several rejections before contacting Cast Art Industries. President Scott Sherman saw the universal appeal of Kristin's creations, and agreed to produce the pieces. The Dreamsicles collection was released in 1991, to much acclaim.

Kristin now lives in a farmhouse in Idaho, where she continues to create designs for Dreamsicles in her studio. "I still get a tingle when I walk into a new store and see my pieces on display," she says. "I never dreamed my cherubs would offer people such comfort and joy."

Cast Art Industries, Inc. Biography

Based in Corona, California, Cast Art Industries, Inc. was founded in December 1990 by Scott Sherman, Frank Colapinto, and Gary Barsellotti. Cast Art catapulted into the national giftware limelight after the March 1991 release of the Dreamsicles collection by artist Kristin Haynes. Among the company's other product lines are Animal Accents, Bumpkins, Ivy & Innocence and Slapstix. You can visit Cast Art's website at *www.castart.com*.

COLLECTOR'S
VALUE GUIDE™

Collectors' Corner

1. Dreamsicles designs are born in a small farmhouse studio where artist Kristin Haynes works her artistic magic, creating prototype sculptures of her adorable cherubs and animals.

2. From the prototype sculpture, production molds are created by experienced Cast Art artisans. A specially formulated, natural gypsum material is then carefully injected into the mold and allowed to dry slowly in a controlled temperature environment.

3. Each individual reproduction is removed from the mold and hand-finished to remove any imperfections. Each step of the production process is carefully monitored to ensure consistent high quality.

4. Next, the delicate hand-painting process begins, as experienced artists apply the subtle pastel shadings and expressive eyes which are the trademark of a Dreamsicles figurine.

5. The final production step is the application of natural dried flowers, which form the decorative wreath. The subtle pastel shades normally used are supplemented with poinsettias and red berries for the Christmas figurines.

6. Most of the finished sculptures are individually packaged. The figurine is inserted into a recycled foam liner for protection and then packaged in a colorful gift box.

7. Dreamsicles are then shipped to retail stores across the country. Retail prices vary, but the figurines typically range from $7 to $30, with larger pieces running between $40-$50. Recent limited edition pieces have retailed from $100 to $150.

COLLECTOR'S
VALUE GUIDE™

Collectors' Corner

Dreamsicles Club News

Due to the rapid popularity of Dreamsicles figurines, Cast Art established the Dreamsicles Club for its fans in 1993. The Club offers a truly special way to enjoy collecting Dreamsicles. Collectors have the opportunity to obtain Symbol of Membership and Members-Only figurines that are not available to the general public, and they receive the Club's quarterly newsletter, *The ClubHouse*, as well as a free copy of this 1998 Dreamsicles Collector's Value Guide™ by Collectors' Publishing, which features full-color pictures of the entire collection and much more. To date, more than 60,000 Dreamsicles enthusiasts have joined the Club.

Dreamsicles Club™
1120 California Ave.
Corona, CA 91719-3324
(800) 437-5818

A one-year membership costs $27.50, while a two-year membership is available for $50.00. Collectors who sign up in 1998 will receive the Symbol Of Membership figurine "Let's Get Together," and will have the opportunity to purchase exclusive Members-Only figurines. In 1997, the Club offered three Members-Only figurines, including the first Club figurine limited to a specific quantity. This piece, "First Blush," was limited to 12,500 pieces and was the first annual figurine in *The Collector's Series*.

Let's Get Together
1998 Symbol Of Membership

In addition to the regular Club offerings, the Club in 1997 introduced two special figurines: "Editor's Choice" and "Golden Halo." The Club presents "Editor's Choice" as a thank you to contributors to *The ClubHouse* newsletter, and awards "Golden Halo" to those who touch the lives of others with extraordinary kindness and courage. These "Good Samaritan" Award winners, as well as Club members who nominate them, receive this special figurine that features a golden wreath.

For more information, see your local retailer or call the Club.

COLLECTOR'S
VALUE GUIDE™

Collectors' Corner

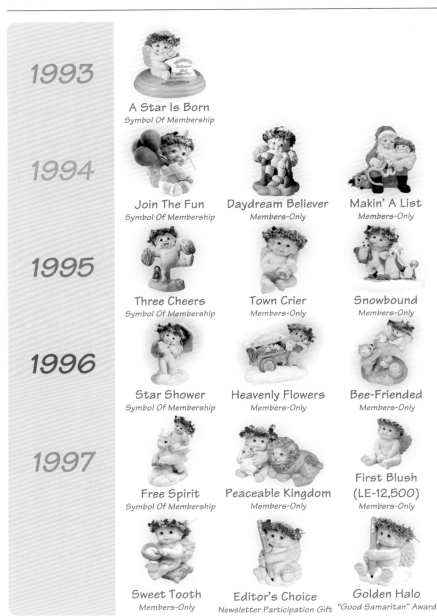

1993

A Star Is Born
Symbol Of Membership

1994

Join The Fun
Symbol Of Membership

Daydream Believer
Members-Only

Makin' A List
Members-Only

1995

Three Cheers
Symbol Of Membership

Town Crier
Members-Only

Snowbound
Members-Only

1996

Star Shower
Symbol Of Membership

Heavenly Flowers
Members-Only

Bee-Friended
Members-Only

1997

Free Spirit
Symbol Of Membership

Peaceable Kingdom
Members-Only

First Blush
(LE-12,500)
Members-Only

Sweet Tooth
Members-Only

Editor's Choice
Newsletter Participation Gift

Golden Halo
"Good Samaritan" Award

COLLECTOR'S
VALUE GUIDE™

Collectors' Corner

Display Tips

Part of the fun of collecting Dreamsicles figurines is sharing them with family and friends, and what better way to share the fun than by displaying your collection for all to see and enjoy. The Dreamsicles cherubs, animals and children themselves can be the inspiration for displays, whether grouped by a particular occasion (such as a wedding, anniversary, graduation or birthday) or by a special theme (such as gardening, animals or sports). Whether your collection is large or small, you can create your own special displays both at home and at work.

Your Dreamsicles display can be as simple or as complex as you want it to be: you can place your figurines along a wall shelf, in a curio cabinet or on an end table. Try varying the height of your displays by placing figurines on books or small boxes covered with fabric, paint, wrapping paper or wallpaper. Add small toys, such as blocks, to create a nursery scene for baby cherubs, or add miniature doll furniture and tiny wrapped packages for a festive birthday party scene.

You can transform a bare shelf into a farm fit for your Dreamsicles animals by making an artificial hay and grass barnyard and adding some miniature fences. Your "Tropical Dreamsicles" will feel right at home on a beach made of coral, sea shells and sand placed in a low-rimmed pan or box. But remember: water can damage your figurines so be sure to keep them high and dry on the beach!

To celebrate the holidays, wrap boxes or blocks of wood in red and silver to highlight your Valentine's Day collection. Hide some plastic eggs in an artificial grass lawn for your Easter cherubs and *Dreamsicles Kids* to find! Cotton snow blankets, plastic snow, miniature Christmas trees and gaily-wrapped packages make a perfect backdrop for your holiday figurines, while the Dreamsicles ornaments can be used to decorate a tree, a wreath or as a special holiday centerpiece. Experimenting with different displays can add a whole new dimension to your Dreamsicles collection. Be creative and have fun!

COLLECTOR'S
VALUE GUIDE™

Glossary

bas-relief—a sculptural process that leaves a raised design, causing the piece to have a three-dimensional appearance.

collectibles—anything and everything that is "able to be collected," whether it's figurines, dolls . . . or even *postcards* can be considered a "collectible," but it is generally recognized that a true collectible should be something that increases in value over time.

current—a piece that is in current production and available in retail stores.

DB (damaged box)—a secondary market term used when an item's original box is in poor condition, thus usually diminishing the value of the item.

Dreamsicles Day—a store-sponsored event that allows collectors the opportunity to meet other collectors, enjoy Dreamsicles-related activities and purchase special event figurines.

early release—a piece released as a "special preview" to selected stores before the piece's scheduled introduction into the general collection.

exchange—a secondary market service that lists pieces that collectors wish to buy or sell. The exchange works as a middleman and usually requires a commission.

exclusive—figurine made especially for, and only available through, a specific store, exposition or buying group.

Gift Creations Concepts (GCC)—a syndicated catalog group that includes over 300 retail stores nationwide. Exclusive pieces and early releases are commonly available through these retailers.

International Collectible Exposition (I.C.E.)—national collectible shows held in Rosemont, Illinois each June or July, and in April alternating between Edison, New Jersey (1998) and Long Beach, California (1999).

issue price—the retail price of an item when it is first introduced. There is no established retail price for Dreamsicles figurines, so prices may vary.

issue year—for Dreamsicles, the year that a piece becomes available in the general collection.

limited edition (LE)—a piece scheduled for a predetermined production quantity or time. Some pieces have been limited to a specific number of pieces (Ex. "Handmade With Love" is limited to 10,000 pieces) or limited by year of production (Ex. the *Christmas Limited Edition*, "All Aboard!," is limited to 1998 production).

markings—any of the various identifying features found on a collectible. It can be information found on bottomstamps or backstamps, an artist's signature or even a symbol denoting a specific year or artist.

Members Only piece—special pieces only available for purchase by members of the Dreamsicles Club.

MIB (mint in box)—a secondary market term used when a collectible item's original box is in "good as new" condition, usually adding to the value of the item.

N.A.L.E.D.—National Association Of Limited Edition Dealers, a retail store trade association.

NB (no box)—a secondary market term used when a collectible item's original box is missing. For most collectibles, having the original box is a factor in the value on the secondary market.

primary market—the conventional collectibles purchasing process in which collectors buy directly from dealers at issue price.

resin—a thick liquid used to bind together different materials for the production of a collectible.

retired—a piece that is taken out of production, never to be made again, usually followed by a scarcity of the piece and an increase in value on the secondary market.

secondary market—the source for buying and selling collectibles according to basic supply-and-demand principles ("pay what the market will bear"). Popular pieces that are sold out or have been retired can appreciate in value far above the original issue price. Pieces are sold through newspaper ads, collector newsletters, the Internet and at collector gatherings.

suspended—a piece that has been removed from production by Cast Art Industries but may return in the future.

swap & sell—event where collectors meet to buy, sell or trade items with each other.

Symbol Of Membership figurine—special piece offered as a gift to collectors joining or renewing their membership to the Dreamsicles Club.

variations—items that have color, design or printed text changes from the "original" piece.

COLLECTOR'S
VALUE GUIDE™

Numerical Index

– Key –

Numerical Index

Numerical Index

Alphabetical Index

153

Alphabetical Index

Alphabetical Index

Alphabetical Index

Alphabetical Index

Alphabetical Index

Alphabetical Index

Notes